CLIVE BARKER was
He is the author of *The*
The Damnation Game, *Weaveworld*, *Cabal*, *The Great and Secret Show*, *The Hellbound Heart*, *Imajica* and *The Thief of Always*. In addition to his work as a novelist and short story writer, he is also an accomplished illustrator and writes, directs and produces for the stage and screen. His spectacular films the *Hellraiser* trilogy, *Nightbreed* and *Candyman* bring his unique and indelible vision of modern horror to celluloid and video life. Barker uses all aspects of popular culture to substantiate his extraordinary insight into the menacing present. Millions of readers and filmgoers have been captivated by Barker's prodigious talents; now graphic novel adaptations of his stories add a further dimension to his hold on the popular imagination. Clive Barker lives in Los Angeles, where he continues his love affair with the bizarre, the perverse and the terrifying.

INTERNATIONAL ACCLAIM FOR
CLIVE BARKER:

'Barker is so good I am almost tongue-tied. What Barker does makes the rest of us look like we've been asleep for the last ten years.'

STEPHEN KING

'A powerful and fascinating writer with a brilliant imagination.'

J.G.BALLARD

'Clive Barker has been an amazing writer from his first appearance, with great gifts of invention and commitment to his own vision stamped on every page.'

PETER STRAUB

BOOKS BY CLIVE BARKER

The Books of Blood (*six volumes*)
The Damnation Game
Weaveworld
Cabal
The Great and Secret Show
The Hellbound Heart
Imajica
The Thief of Always

GRAPHIC STORIES BY CLIVE BARKER

The Yattering and Jack
Tapping the Vein (*five volumes*)
Son of Celluloid
Clive Barker Illustrator

THE ARTISTS

Dan Brereton
is a native of the San Francisco Bay area. His second professional comics work, the *Black Terror* mini-series, won him the coveted Russ Manning Award for Promising Newcomer in 1990. He went on to paint *The Psycho* for DC Comics, and, since finishing *Dread*, has been at work on a prestige *World's Finest* mini-series. Brereton is an avid collector of toys, and he and his family share their home with a pair of man-eating fish, two snakes, Lucifer and Polychrome, and an iguana named Cleo.

Tim Conrad
was born in 1951 in Springfield, Illinois. He has illustrated graphic adaptations of the Robert E. Howard characters Conan, Bran Mak Morn and Almuric, as well as many science fiction short stories, including the graphic novel *Etc*, and the horror graphic novel *Toadswart D'Amplestone*. He still lives in Illinois, where he has served as a bank vice-president. In addition to illustrating graphic novels, he is an advertising copywriter.

CLIVE BARKER

DREAD

Adapted by Fred Burke
Illustrated by Dan Brereton

AND

DOWN SATAN

Adapted by Steve Niles
Illustrated by Tim Conrad

EclipseGraphicNovels
An Imprint of HarperCollins*Publishers*

Eclipse Graphic Novels
An Imprint of HarperCollins*Publishers*,
77–85 Fulham Palace Road,
Hammersmith, London W6 8JB

Published by Eclipse Graphic Novels 1993

9 8 7 6 5 4 3 2 1

ISBN 0 586 21755 X

Printed and bound in Hong Kong

THERE IS NO DELIGHT THE EQUAL OF DREAD.
IF IT WERE POSSIBLE TO SIT, INVISIBLE, BETWEEN TWO PEOPLE ON ANY TRAIN, IN ANY WAITING ROOM OR OFFICE, THE CONVERSATION WOULD TIME AND AGAIN CIRCLE ON THAT SUBJECT.
MURDER IN KENSINGTON

CERTAINLY THE DEBATE MIGHT APPEAR TO BE ABOUT SOMETHING ENTIRELY DIFFERENT...

...THE STATE OF THE NATION, IDLE CHAT ABOUT DEATH ON THE ROADS, THE RISING PRICE OF DENTAL CARE...
TELEPHONE

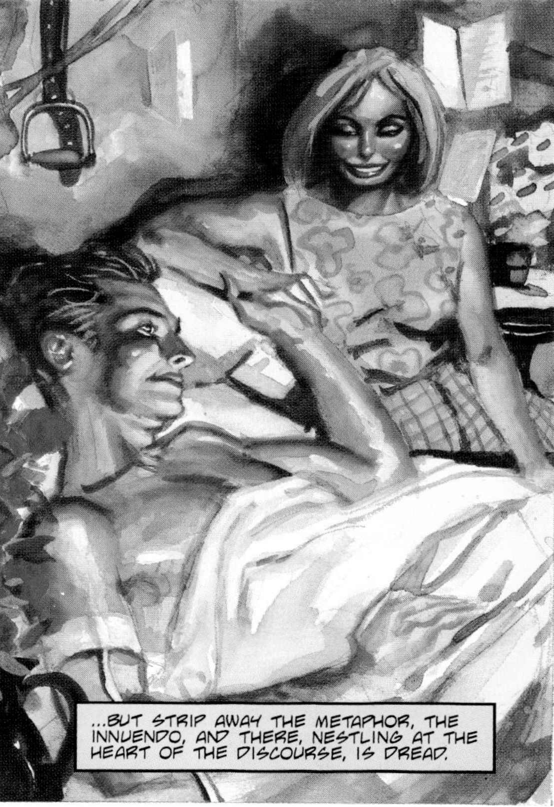
...BUT STRIP AWAY THE METAPHOR, THE INNUENDO, AND THERE, NESTLING AT THE HEART OF THE DISCOURSE, IS DREAD.

WHILE THE NATURE OF GOD AND THE POSSIBILITY OF ETERNAL LIFE GO UNDISCUSSED, WE HAPPILY CHEW OVER THE MINUTIAE OF MISERY.

THE SYNDROME RECOGNIZES NO BOUNDARIES; IN BATHHOUSE AND SEMINAR ROOM ALIKE, THE SAME RITUAL IS REPEATED.

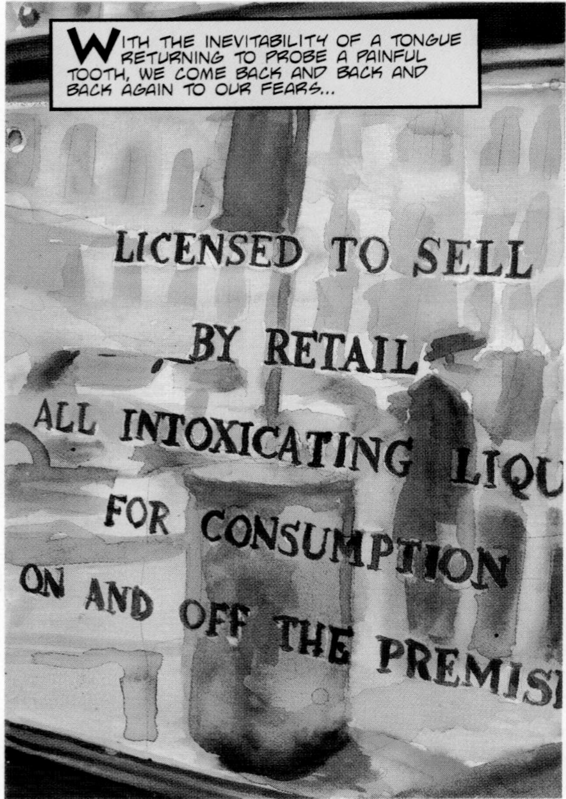
WITH THE INEVITABILITY OF A TONGUE RETURNING TO PROBE A PAINFUL TOOTH, WE COME BACK AND BACK AND BACK AGAIN TO OUR FEARS...
LICENSED TO SELL
BY RETAIL
ALL INTOXICATING LIQU
FOR CONSUMPTION
ON AND OFF THE PREMISI

...SITTING TO TALK THEM OVER WITH THE EAGERNESS OF A HUNGRY MAN BEFORE A FULL AND STEAMING PLATE.

WHILE HE WAS STILL AT UNIVERSITY, AND AFRAID TO SPEAK, STEPHEN GRACE WAS TAUGHT TO SPEAK OF WHY HE WAS AFRAID. IN FACT, NOT SIMPLY TO TALK ABOUT IT, BUT TO ANALYZE AND DISSECT HIS EVERY NERVE-ENDING, LOOKING FOR TINY TERRORS.
IN THIS INVESTIGATION, HE HAD A TEACHER: QUAID.
IT WAS AN AGE OF GURUS; IT WAS THEIR SEASON. IN UNIVERSITIES UP AND DOWN ENGLAND YOUNG MEN AND WOMEN WERE LOOKING EAST AND WEST FOR PEOPLE TO FOLLOW LIKE LAMBS.
IT WAS HIS BAD LUCK THAT QUAID WAS THE MESSIAH HE FOUND.

THE NAME'S QUAID. YOU'RE--?
STEVE GRACE.
YES--YOU'RE IN THE ETHICS CLASS, RIGHT? I DON'T SEE YOU IN ANY OF THE OTHER PHILOSOPHY SEMINARS OR LECTURES...

IT'S MY EXTRA SUBJECT FOR THE YEAR. I'M ON THE ENGLISH LITERATURE COURSE. I JUST COULDN'T BEAR THE IDEA OF A YEAR IN THE OLD NORSE CLASSES.
SO YOU PLUMPED FOR ETHICS-- A DOUBLE BRANDY FOR ME, BARMAN. WHAT ARE YOU HAVING?
A DOUBLE BRANDY WOULD HAVE JUST ABOUT CRIPPLED STEVE'S FINANCES FOR THE NEXT WEEK. QUAID DIDN'T LOOK *THAT* WELL OFF. STEVE HIMSELF HAD PLANNED TO NURSE HALF A PINT OF LUKEWARM LAGER FOR AT LEAST AN HOUR.

NOTHING FOR ME.
YES, YOU WILL.
I'M FINE.
AND A PINT OF LAGER FOR MY FRIEND.
STEVE DIDN'T RESIST QUAID'S GENEROSITY. A PINT AND A HALF OF LAGER IN HIS UNFED SYSTEM WOULD HELP NO END IN DULLING THE TEDIUM OF HIS ONCOMING SEMINARS ON "CHARLES DICKENS AS A SOCIAL ANALYST." HE YAWNED JUST TO THINK OF IT.

SOMEBODY OUGHT TO WRITE A THESIS ON DRINKING AS A SOCIAL ACTIVITY.

OR AS OBLIVION.

STEVE LOOKED AT THE MAN. PERHAPS FIVE YEARS OLDER THAN STEVE'S TWENTY. THE MIXTURE OF CLOTHES HE WORE WAS CONFUSING.
THE FACE WAS UNREMARKABLE, THE EYES MILKY-BLUE AND SO PALE THAT THE COLOR SEEMED TO SEEP INTO THE WHITES, LEAVING JUST THE PINPRICKS OF HIS IRISES BEHIND HIS HEAVY GLASSES.
QUAID, STEVE DECIDED, COULD HAVE PASSED FOR A DUTCH DOPE PUSHER.
HE WORE NO BADGES. THEY WERE THE COMMON CURRENCY OF A STUDENT'S OBSESSIONS, AND QUAID LOOKED NAKED WITHOUT SOMETHING TO IMPLY HOW HE TOOK HIS PLEASURES. WAS HE A GAY, FEMINIST, SAVE-THE-WHALE CAMPAIGNER? OR A FASCIST VEGETARIAN? WHAT WAS HE INTO, FOR GOD'S SAKE?

YOU SHOULD HAVE BEEN DOING OLD NORSE.
WHY?
THEY DON'T EVEN BOTHER TO MARK THE PAPERS ON THAT COURSE.
STEVE HADN'T HEARD ABOUT THIS.

THEY JUST THROW THEM ALL UP INTO THE AIR. FACE UP, AN "A". FACE DOWN, A "B".

OH. IT WAS A JOKE. QUAID WAS BEING WITTY.
YOU SHOULD BE IN OLD NORSE. WHO NEEDS BISHOP BERKELEY ANYHOW? OR PLATO. OR--
OR?
IT'S ALL SHIT.
YES.

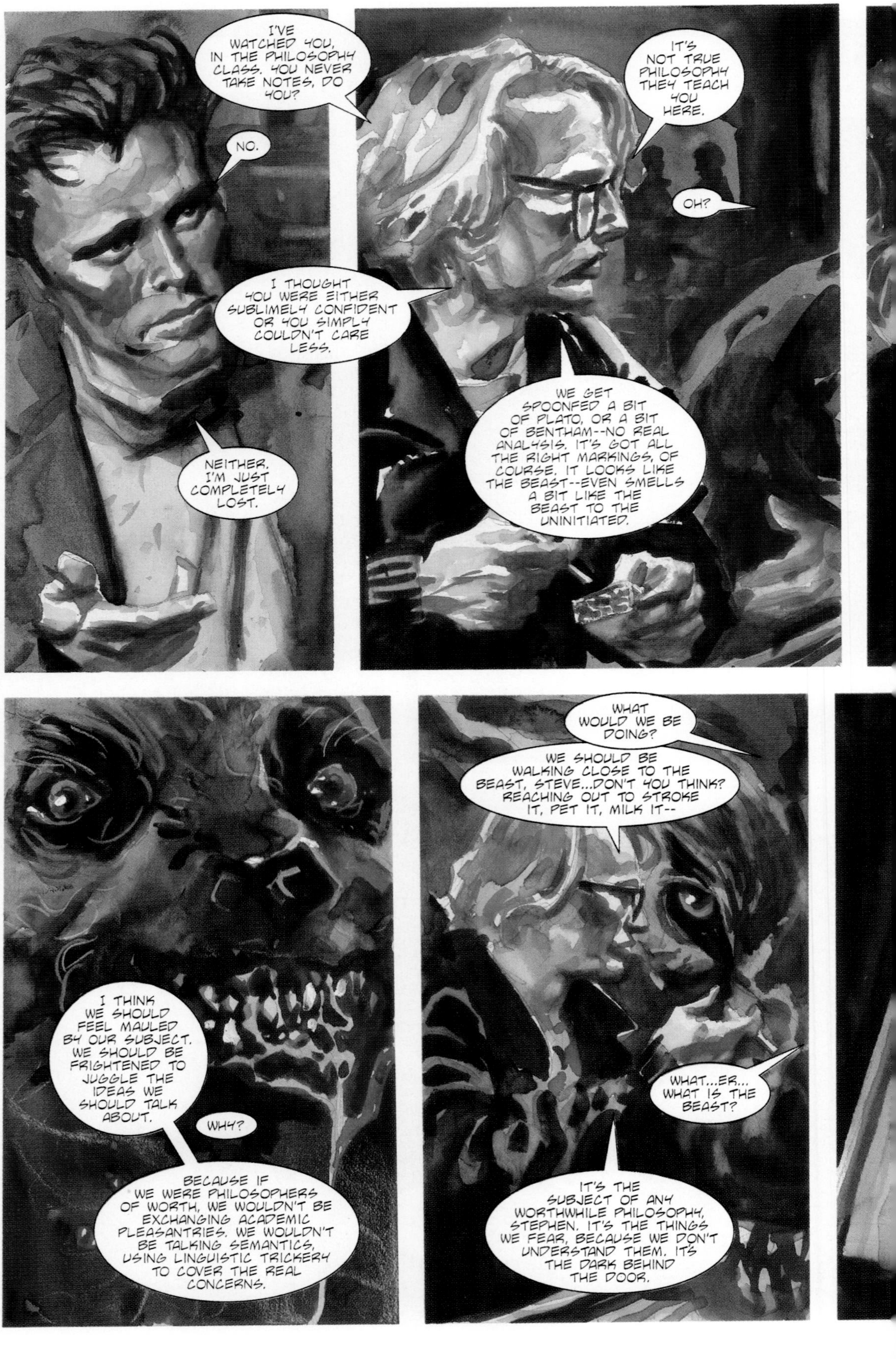

I'VE WATCHED YOU, IN THE PHILOSOPHY CLASS. YOU NEVER TAKE NOTES, DO YOU?
NO.
I THOUGHT YOU WERE EITHER SUBLIMELY CONFIDENT OR YOU SIMPLY COULDN'T CARE LESS.
NEITHER. I'M JUST COMPLETELY LOST.
IT'S NOT TRUE PHILOSOPHY THEY TEACH YOU HERE.
OH?
WE GET SPOONFED A BIT OF PLATO, OR A BIT OF BENTHAM--NO REAL ANALYSIS. IT'S GOT ALL THE RIGHT MARKINGS, OF COURSE. IT LOOKS LIKE THE BEAST--EVEN SMELLS A BIT LIKE THE BEAST TO THE UNINITIATED.

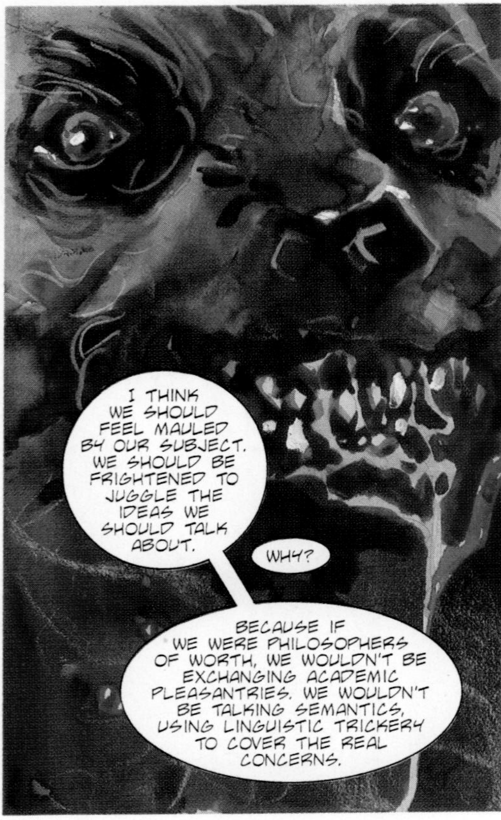

THE CIGARETTES WERE CHEAP--AGAIN, NOT THE DONE THING. OU EITHER SMOKED GAULOISES, AMEL, OR NOTHING AT ALL.
WHAT BEAST?
PHILOSOPHY. TRUE PHILOSOPHY. IT'S A BEAST, STEPHEN--DON'T YOU THINK?
I HADN'T--
IT'S WILD. IT BITES.

YES. IT BITES.
BITES.
STEPHEN NODDED. THE METAPHOR WAS BEYOND HIM.

TEVE THOUGHT OF A DOOR. THOUGHT OF HE DARK. HE BEGAN O SEE WHAT QUAID AS DRIVING AT HIS LABYRINTHINE ASHION. PHILOSOPHY AS A WAY TO TALK BOUT FEAR.
WE SHOULD SCUSS WHAT'S IMATE TO OUR YCHES. IF WE DON'T, WE RISK...
WHAT?
WANT ANOTHER?
STEVE PRAYED THAT THE ANSWER WOULD BE NO.

WHAT DO WE RISK?
WELL, I THINK IF WE DON'T GO OUT AND FIND THE BEAST--
--SOONER OR LATER, THE BEAST WILL COME AND FIND US.
THERE IS NO DELIGHT THE EQUAL OF DREAD. AS LONG AS IT'S SOMEONE ELSE'S.

CASUALLY, IN THE FOLLOWING WEEK OR TWO, STEVE MADE SOME ENQUIRIES ABOUT THE CURIOUS MR. QUAID.
NOBODY KNEW HIS FIRST NAME.
NOBODY WAS CERTAIN OF HIS AGE--
--BUT ONE OF THE SECRETARIES THOUGHT HE WAS OVER THIRTY, WHICH CAME AS A SURPRISE.
HIS PARENTS, CHERYL HAD HEARD HIM SAY, WERE DEAD.
KILLED, SHE THOUGHT.
THAT APPEARED TO BE THE SUM OF HUMAN KNOWLEDGE WHERE QUAID WAS CONCERNED.
I OWE YOU A DRINK, BRANDY?
THANK YOU.
BRERETON 19 91

DID I STARTLE YOU?
I WAS THINKING.
NO PHILOSOPHER SHOULD BE WITHOUT ONE.
ONE WHAT?
BRAIN.

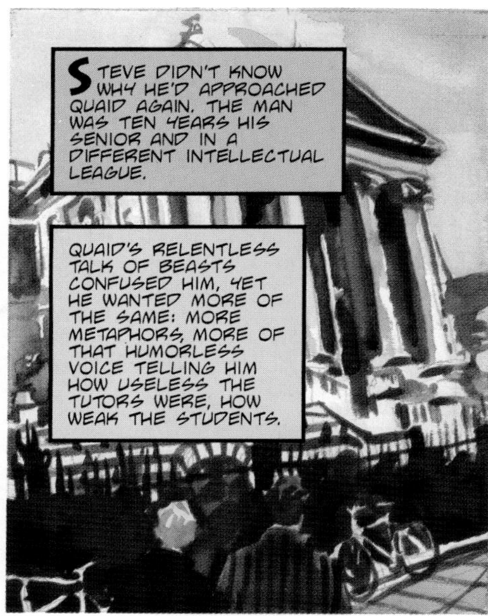
STEVE DIDN'T KNOW WHY HE'D APPROACHED QUAID AGAIN. THE MAN WAS TEN YEARS HIS SENIOR AND IN A DIFFERENT INTELLECTUAL LEAGUE.
QUAID'S RELENTLESS TALK OF BEASTS CONFUSED HIM, YET HE WANTED MORE OF THE SAME: MORE METAPHORS, MORE OF THAT HUMORLESS VOICE TELLING HIM HOW USELESS THE TUTORS WERE, HOW WEAK THE STUDENTS.

IN QUAID'S WORLD THERE WERE NO CERTAINTIES. HE HAD NO SECULAR GURUS AND CERTAINLY NO RELIGION. HE SEEMED INCAPABLE OF VIEWING ANY SYSTEM, WHETHER IT WAS POLITICAL OR PHILOSOPHICAL, WITHOUT CYNICISM.
THOUGH HE SELDOM LAUGHED OUT LOUD, STEVE KNEW THERE WAS A BITTER HUMOR IN HIS VISION OF THE WORLD. PEOPLE WERE LAMBS AND SHEEP, ALL LOOKING FOR SHEPHERDS.
OF COURSE, THESE SHEPHERDS WERE FICTIONS, IN QUAID'S OPINION. ALL THAT EXISTED, IN THE DARKNESS OUTSIDE THE SHEEP-FOLD, WERE THE FEARS THAT FIXED ON THE INNOCENT MUTTON, FEARS WAITING, PATIENT AS STONE, FOR THEIR MOMENT.
EVERYTHING WAS TO BE DOUBTED, BUT THE FACT THAT DREAD EXISTED.

QUAID'S INTELLECTUAL ARROGANCE WAS EXHILARATING. STEVE SOON CAME TO LOVE THE ICONOCLASTIC EASE WITH WHICH HE DEMOLISHED BELIEF AFTER BELIEF. SOMETIMES IT WAS PAINFUL WHEN QUAID FORMULATED A WATERTIGHT ARGUMENT AGAINST ONE OF STEVE'S DOGMA--
--BUT AFTER A FEW WEEKS, EVEN THE SOUND OF THE DEMOLITION SEEMED TO EXCITE. QUAID WAS CLEARING THE UNDERGROWTH, FELLING THE TREES, RAZING THE STUBBLE. STEVE FELT FREE.
NATION, FAMILY, CHURCH, LAW. ALL ASH. ALL USELESS. ALL CHEATS, AND CHAINS, AND SUFFOCATION.

THERE WAS ONLY DREAD.
I FEAR, YOU FEAR, WE FEAR. HE, SHE, OR IT FEARS.
THERE'S NO CONSCIOUS THING ON THE FACE OF THE WORLD THAT DOESN'T KNOW DREAD MORE INTIMATELY THAN ITS OWN HEARTBEAT.

ONE OF QUAID'S FAVORITE BAITING-VICTIMS WAS ANOTHER PHILOSOPHY AND ENG. LIT. STUDENT, CHERYL FROMM.

AND YOU'RE FULL OF SHIT! SO WHO CARES IF YOU'RE AFRAID OF YOUR OWN SHADOW? I'M NOT. I FEEL FINE.

SHE WOULD RISE TO HIS MORE OUTRAGEOUS REMARKS LIKE FISH TO RAIN. CHERYL WAS, IN QUAID'S PHRASE, A PATHOLOGICAL OPTIMIST.

SHE CERTAINLY LOOKED IT. CHERYL FROMM WAS WET DREAM MATERIAL, BUT TOO BRIGHT FOR ANYONE TO TRY MAKING A MOVE ON HER.

WE ALL TASTE DREAD ONCE IN A WHILE.

QUAID'S MILKY EYES STUDIED HER FACE INTENTLY, WATCHING FOR HER REACTION, TRYING, STEVE KNEW, TO FIND A FLAW IN HER CONVICTION.

I DON'T.

NO FEARS? NO NIGHTMARES?

NO WAY. I'VE GOT A GOOD FAMILY. I DON'T HAVE ANY SKELETONS IN MY CLOSET. I DON'T EVEN EAT MEAT, SO I DON'T FEEL BAD WHEN I DRIVE PAST A SLAUGHTERHOUSE. I DON'T HAVE ANY SHIT TO PUT ON SHOW. DOES THAT MEAN I'M NOT REAL?

IT MEANS-- IT MEANS YOUR CONFIDENCE HAS SOMETHING BIG TO COVER.

BACK TO NIGHTMARES.

BIG NIGHTMARES.

BE SPECIFIC: DEFINE YOUR TERMS.

I CAN'T TELL YOU WHAT YOU FEAR.

TELL ME WHAT *YOU* FEAR THEN.

FINALLY, IT'S BEYOND ANALYSIS.
BEYOND ANALYSIS, MY ASS!
WHAT I FEAR IS PERSONAL TO ME. IT MAKES NO SENSE IN A LARGER CONTEXT.
THE SIGNS OF MY DREAD, THE IMAGES MY BRAIN USES, IF YOU LIKE, TO *ILLUSTRATE* MY FEAR, THOSE SIGNS ARE MILD STUFF BY COMPARISON WITH THE REAL HORROR THAT'S AT THE ROOT OF MY PERSONALITY.

HE STOPPED, REGRETTING THE CONFESSION ALREADY.
I'VE GOT IMAGES. PICTURES FROM CHILDHOOD THAT MAKE ME THINK OF--
WHAT? YOU MEAN THINGS TO DO WITH BAD EXPERIENCES? LIKE FALLING OFF YOUR BIKE--SOMETHING LIKE THAT?

PERHAPS.
I FIND MYSELF, SOMETIMES, THINKING OF THOSE PICTURES. NOT DELIBERATELY, JUST WHEN MY CONCENTRATION'S IDLING. IT'S ALMOST AS THOUGH MY MIND WENT TO THEM AUTOMATICALLY.
PRECISELY.
FREUD WRITES ON THAT.

PLEASE, CHERYL--MOTHER FIXATIONS DON'T ANSWER THE PROBLEM. THE REAL TERRORS IN ME, IN ALL OF US, ARE PRE-PERSONALITY.
DREAD'S THERE BEFORE WE HAVE ANY NOTION OF OURSELVES AS INDIVIDUALS. THE THUMB-NAIL, CURLED UP ON ITSELF IN THE WOMB, FEELS FEAR.

YOU REMEMBER, DO YOU?
MAYBE.
THE *WOMB?*

IT WAS A WEIRD, UNPLEASANT SMILE, ONE STEVE WANTED TO WASH OFF HIS EYES. HE THOUGHT THE SMILE SAID: "I HAVE KNOWLEDGE YOU DON'T."

YOU'RE A LIAR.
PERHAPS I AM.

AFTER THAT THE DEBATE STOPPED. NO MORE TALKING ABOUT NIGHTMARES. NO MORE DEBATING THE THINGS THAT GO BUMP IN THE NIGHT. STEVE SAW QUAID IRREGULARLY FOR THE NEXT MONTH, AND WHEN HE DID, QUAID WAS INVARIABLY IN THE COMPANY OF CHERYL FROMM.

NO SMOKING
QUAID WAS POLITE WITH HER, EVEN DEFERENTIAL. HE NO LONGER WORE HIS LEATHER JACKET, BECAUSE SHE HATED THE SMELL OF DEAD ANIMAL MATTER.

THIS SUDDEN CHANGE IN THEIR RELATIONSHIP CONFOUNDED STEPHEN, BUT HE PUT IT DOWN TO HIS PRIMITIVE UNDERSTANDING OF SEXUAL MATTERS. HE WASN'T A VIRGIN, BUT WOMEN WERE STILL A MYSTERY TO HIM, CONTRADICTORY AND PUZZLING.

HE WAS ALSO JEALOUS, THOUGH HE WOULDN'T ENTIRELY ADMIT THAT OF HIMSELF. HE RESENTED THE FACT THAT THE WET DREAM GENIUS WAS TAKING UP SO MUCH OF QUAID'S TIME.
THERE WAS ANOTHER FEELING, A CURIOUS SENSE HE HAD THAT QUAID WAS COURTING CHERYL FOR HIS OWN STRANGE REASONS.
SEX WAS NOT QUAID'S MOTIVE, HE FELT SURE. NOR WAS IT RESPECT FOR CHERYL'S INTELLIGENCE THAT MADE HIM SO ATTENTIVE.

NO, HE WAS CORNERING HER SOMEHOW, THAT WAS STEVE'S INSTINCT.
CHERYL FROMM WAS BEING ROUNDED UP FOR THE KILL.

SHE'S A VEGETARIAN.
CHERYL?
OF COURSE, CHERYL.
I KNOW. SHE MENTIONED IT BEFORE.
PIZZA

YES, BUT IT ISN'T A FAD WITH HER. SHE'S PASSIONATE ABOUT IT. CAN'T EVEN BEAR TO LOOK IN A BUTCHER'S WINDOW. SHE WON'T TOUCH MEAT, SMELL MEAT--
OH.
DREAD, STEVE.
OF MEAT?

THE SIGNS ARE DIFFERENT FROM PERSON TO PERSON. *SHE FEARS MEAT*. SHE SAYS SHE'S SO HEALTHY, SO BALANCED. SHIT! I'LL FIND IT--
FIND WHAT?
THE *FEAR*, STEVE.

YOU'RE NOT GOING TO...?

HARM HER? NO, I'M NOT GOING TO HARM HER IN ANY WAY. ANY DAMAGE DONE TO HER WILL BE STRICTLY... *SELF-* INFLICTED.

IT'S ABOUT TIME WE LEARNED TO TRUST ONE ANOTHER. BETWEEN THE TWO OF US--
LISTEN, I DON'T THINK I WANT TO HEAR.
WE HAVE TO TOUCH THE BEAST, STEPHEN.

DAMN THE BEAST...
...I DON'T WANT TO HEAR!

WE'RE FRIENDS, STEPHEN
YES...
THEN RESPECT THAT.

SILENCE. NOT A WORD.

STEVE NODDED. THAT WASN'T A DIFFICULT PROMISE TO KEEP. THERE WAS NOBODY HE COULD TELL HIS ANXIETIES TO WITHOUT BEING LAUGHED AT.
LOOKING SATISFIED, QUAID HURRIED AWAY, LEAVING STEVE FEELING AS THOUGH HE HAD UNWILLINGLY JOINED SOME SECRET SOCIETY, FOR WHAT PURPOSE HE COULDN'T BEGIN TO TELL.
QUAID HAD MADE A PACT WITH HIM, AND IT WAS UNNERVING.

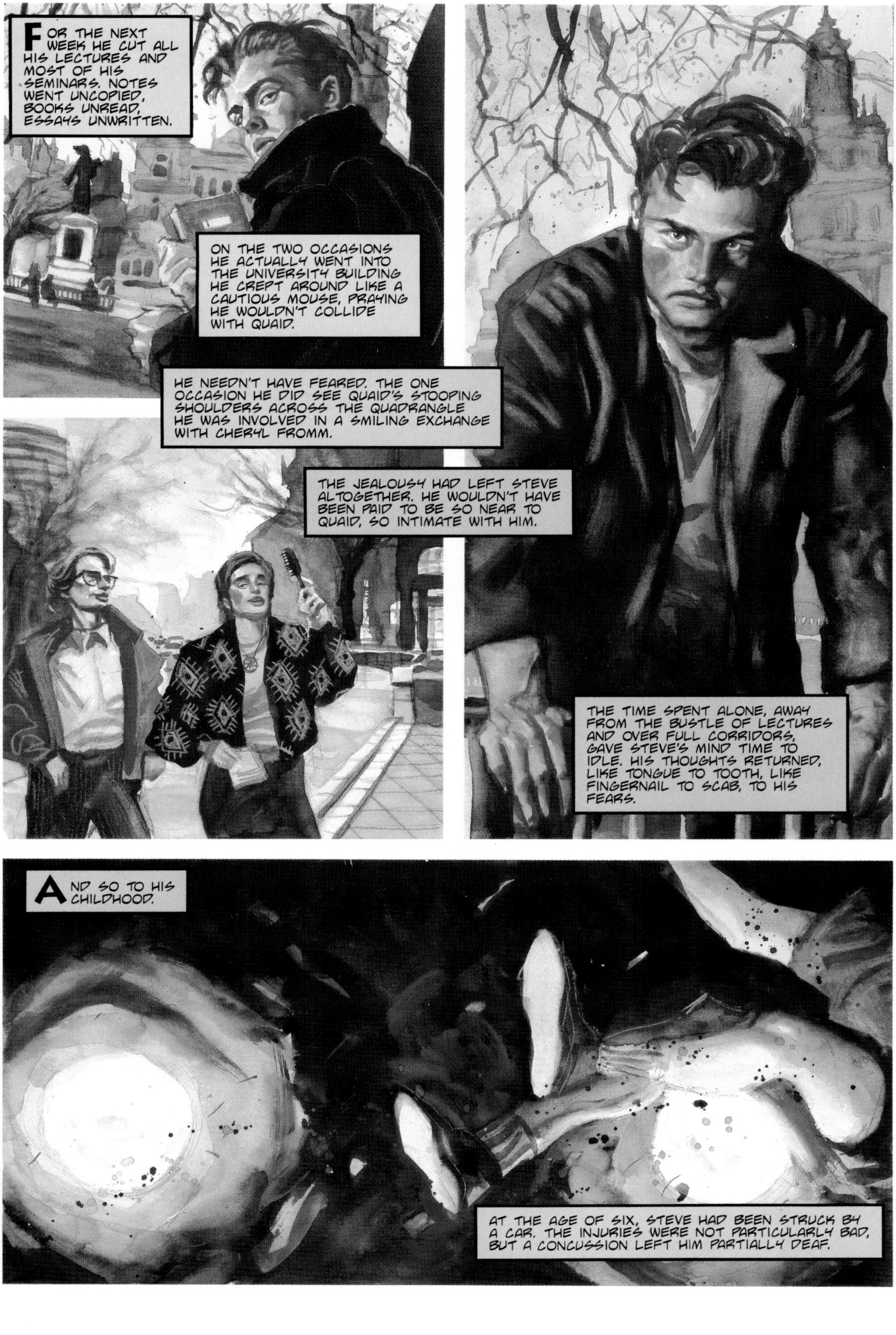

FOR THE NEXT WEEK HE CUT ALL HIS LECTURES AND MOST OF HIS SEMINARS. NOTES WENT UNCOPIED, BOOKS UNREAD, ESSAYS UNWRITTEN.

ON THE TWO OCCASIONS HE ACTUALLY WENT INTO THE UNIVERSITY BUILDING HE CREPT AROUND LIKE A CAUTIOUS MOUSE, PRAYING HE WOULDN'T COLLIDE WITH QUAID.

HE NEEDN'T HAVE FEARED. THE ONE OCCASION HE DID SEE QUAID'S STOOPING SHOULDERS ACROSS THE QUADRANGLE HE WAS INVOLVED IN A SMILING EXCHANGE WITH CHERYL FROMM.

THE JEALOUSY HAD LEFT STEVE ALTOGETHER. HE WOULDN'T HAVE BEEN PAID TO BE SO NEAR TO QUAID, SO INTIMATE WITH HIM.

THE TIME SPENT ALONE, AWAY FROM THE BUSTLE OF LECTURES AND OVER FULL CORRIDORS, GAVE STEVE'S MIND TIME TO IDLE. HIS THOUGHTS RETURNED, LIKE TONGUE TO TOOTH, LIKE FINGERNAIL TO SCAB, TO HIS FEARS.

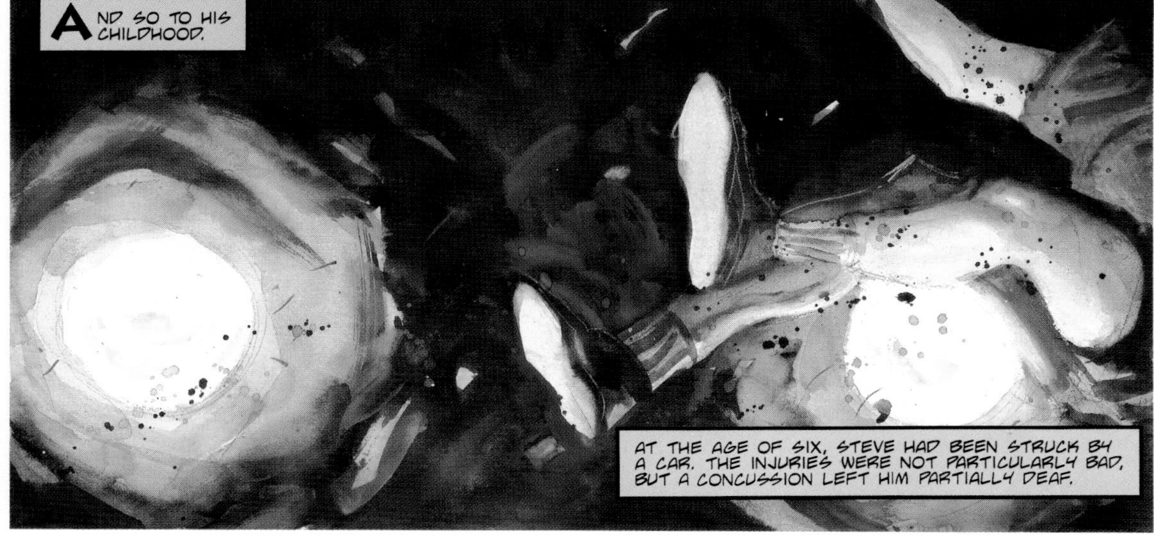

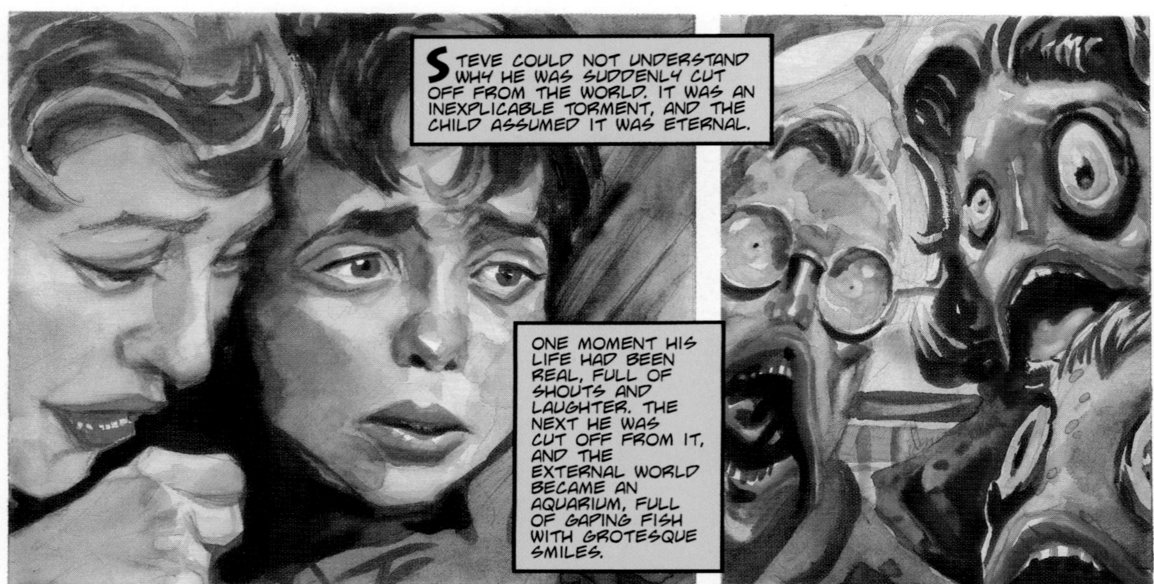
STEVE COULD NOT UNDERSTAND WHY HE WAS SUDDENLY CUT OFF FROM THE WORLD. IT WAS AN INEXPLICABLE TORMENT, AND THE CHILD ASSUMED IT WAS ETERNAL.
ONE MOMENT HIS LIFE HAD BEEN REAL, FULL OF SHOUTS AND LAUGHTER. THE NEXT HE WAS CUT OFF FROM IT, AND THE EXTERNAL WORLD BECAME AN AQUARIUM, FULL OF GAPING FISH WITH GROTESQUE SMILES.

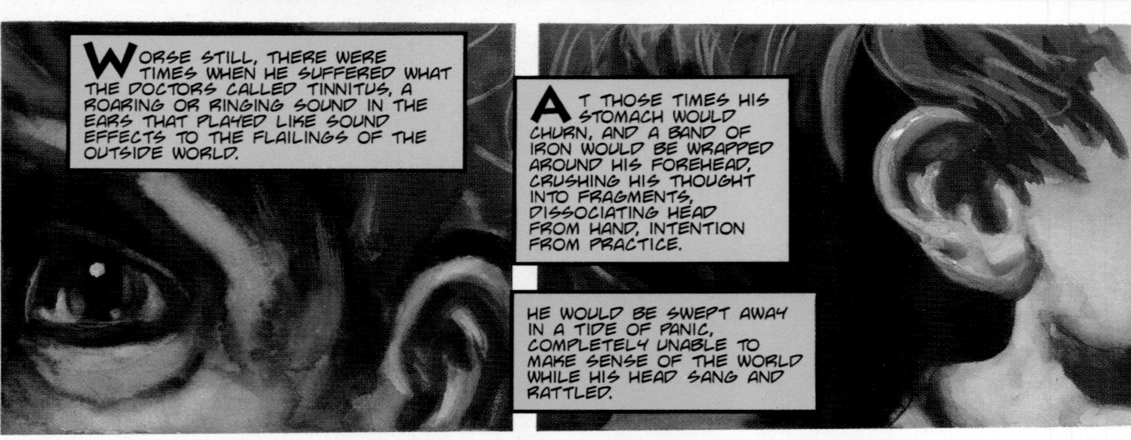
WORSE STILL, THERE WERE TIMES WHEN HE SUFFERED WHAT THE DOCTORS CALLED TINNITUS, A ROARING OR RINGING SOUND IN THE EARS THAT PLAYED LIKE SOUND EFFECTS TO THE FLAILINGS OF THE OUTSIDE WORLD.
AT THOSE TIMES HIS STOMACH WOULD CHURN, AND A BAND OF IRON WOULD BE WRAPPED AROUND HIS FOREHEAD, CRUSHING HIS THOUGHT INTO FRAGMENTS, DISSOCIATING HEAD FROM HAND, INTENTION FROM PRACTICE.
HE WOULD BE SWEPT AWAY IN A TIDE OF PANIC, COMPLETELY UNABLE TO MAKE SENSE OF THE WORLD WHILE HIS HEAD SANG AND RATTLED.

BUT AT NIGHT CAME THE WORST TERRORS. HE WOULD WAKE, SOMETIMES, IN WHAT HAD BEEN (BEFORE THE ACCIDENT) THE REASSURING WOMB OF HIS BEDROOM, TO FIND THE TINGING HAD BEGUN IN HIS SLEEP.
HIS MIND WOULD BE FILLED WITH THE MOST RAUCOUS DIN, WHICH HE WAS LOCKED IN WITH, BEYOND HOPE OF REPRIEVE. NOTHING COULD SILENCE HIS HEAD, AND NOTHING, IT SEEMED, COULD BRING THE WORLD--THE SPEAKING, LAUGHING, CRYING WORLD--BACK TO HIM.
HE WAS ALONE.

THAT WAS THE BEGINNING, MIDDLE, AND END OF THE DREAD. HE WAS ABSOLUTELY ALONE WITH HIS CACOPHONY. LOCKED IN THIS HOUSE, IN THIS ROOM, IN THIS BODY, IN THIS HEAD, A PRISONER OF DEAF, BLIND FLESH.
IT WAS ALMOST UNBEARABLE. IN THE NIGHT THE BOY WOULD SOMETIMES CRY OUT, NOT KNOWING HE WAS MAKING ANY SOUND...

...AND THE FISH WHO HAD BEEN HIS PARENTS WOULD TURN ON THE LIGHT AND COME TO TRY AND HELP HIM...
...BENDING OVER HIS BED MAKING FACES, THEIR SOUNDLESS MOUTHS FORMING UGLY SHAPES IN THEIR ATTEMPTS TO HELP.
THEIR TOUCHES WOULD CALM HIM AT LAST; WITH TIME HIS MOTHER LEARNED THE TRICK OF SOOTHING AWAY THE PANIC THAT SWEPT OVER HIM.

A WEEK BEFORE HIS SEVENTH BIRTHDAY, HIS HEARING RETURNED, NOT PERFECTLY, BUT WELL ENOUGH FOR IT TO SEEM LIKE A MIRACLE. THE WORLD SNAPPED BACK INTO FOCUS, AND LIFE BEGAN AFRESH.
IT TOOK SEVERAL MONTHS FOR THE BOY TO TRUST HIS SENSES AGAIN. HE WOULD STILL WAKE IN THE NIGHT, HALF-ANTICIPATING THE HEAD NOISES.
BUT THOUGH HIS EARS WOULD RING AT THE SLIGHTEST VOLUME OF SOUND, HE NOW SCARCELY EVER NOTICED HIS SLIGHT DEAFNESS.
HE REMEMBERED, OF COURSE. VERY WELL. HE COULD BRING BACK THE TASTE OF HIS PANIC, THE FEEL OF THE IRON BAND AROUND HIS HEAD. AND THERE WAS A RESIDUE OF FEAR THERE--OF THE DARK, OF BEING ALONE.

BUT THEN, WASN'T EVERYONE AFRAID TO BE ALONE? TO BE UTTERLY ALONE...

STEVE HAD ANOTHER FEAR NOW, FAR MORE DIFFICULT TO PIN DOWN.
QUAID.
IN A DRUNKEN REVELATION SESSION HE HAD TOLD QUAID ABOUT HIS CHILDHOOD, ABOUT HIS DEAFNESS, ABOUT HIS NIGHT TERRORS.
QUAID KNEW ABOUT HIS WEAKNESS: THE CLEAR ROUTE INTO THE HEART OF STEVE'S DREAD. HE HAD A WEAPON, A STICK TO BEAT STEVE WITH, SHOULD IT EVER COME TO THAT. MAYBE THAT WAS WHY STEVE CHOSE NOT TO SPEAK TO CHERYL (WARN HER, WAS THAT WHAT HE WANTED TO DO?) AND CERTAINLY THAT WAS WHY HE AVOIDED QUAID.
THE MAN HAD A LOOK, IN CERTAIN MOODS, OF MALICE. NOTHING MORE OR LESS. HE LOOKED LIKE A MAN WITH MALICE DEEP, DEEP IN HIM.
MAYBE THOSE FOUR MONTHS OF WATCHING PEOPLE WITH THE SOUND TURNED DOWN HAD SENSITIZED STEVE TO THE TINY GLANCES, SNEERS, AND SMILES THAT FLIT ACROSS PEOPLE'S FACES. HE KNEW QUAID WAS A LABYRINTH; A MAP OF ITS COMPLEXITIES WAS ETCHED ON HIS FACE IN A THOUSAND TINY EXPRESSIONS.

"NICE PHOTO, DON'T YOU THINK? LOOK AT THE EXPRESSION OF DISGUST ON HER FACE. SHE HATED EVEN THE SMELL OF COOKED MEAT. SHE WASN'T HUNGRY THEN, OF COURSE."

LETS SEE... SLEEPING...DRINKING... SLEEPING AGAIN... PISSING...
HOW LONG HAS SHE BEEN IN THE ROOM?

"THIS WAS ONLY FOURTEEN HOURS IN. SHE LOST ORIENTATION AS TO TIME VERY QUICKLY. NO LIGHT CHANGE, YOU SEE. HER BODY CLOCK WAS FUCKED UP PRETTY SOON."
"HOW LONG WAS SHE IN THERE?"
"TIL THE POINT WAS PROVED."

"THIS WAS TAKEN THE FOLLOWING MORNING. I WAS ASLEEP--THE CAMERA JUST TOOK PICTURES EVERY QUARTER HOUR. LOOK AT HER EYES..."
"SHE LOOKS SICK."
"SHE'S TIRED, THAT'S ALL. SHE DOESN'T KNOW NOW IF IT'S DAY OR NIGHT. AND SHE'S HUNGRY, OF COURSE. IT'S BEEN A DAY AND A HALF. SHE'S MORE THAN A LITTLE PECKISH."

SHE SLEPT A LOT, AS IT HAPPENED, BUT IT SEEMED JUST TO MAKE HER MORE EXHAUSTED THAN EVER. I REPLACED THE WATER JUG WHEN SHE WAS ASLEEP. I COULD HAVE DONE A JIG IN THERE AND IT WOULDN'T HAVE WOKEN HER. LOST TO THE WORLD.
MAD, THOUGHT STEVE. THE MAN'S MAD.
GOD, IT STANK IN THERE. YOU KNOW HOW WOMEN SMELL SOMETIMES--IT'S NOT SWEAT, IT'S SOMETHING ELSE. HEAVY ODOR. MEATY. BLOODY. SHE CAME ON TOWARDS THE END OF HER TIME. HADN'T PLANNED IT WAY.

"THIS IS WHERE THE CRACKS BEGIN TO SHOW. THIS WHERE THE DREAD BEGINS."

"SHE ALWAYS ENDED UP HARANGUING ME, WHENEVER SHE'D HAD A CONFRONTATION WITH THE MEAT. THIS IS COMING UP ON THREE DAYS. YOU'RE LOOKING AT A HUNGRY WOMAN."

"YOU--YOU'RE STARVING HER."
"SHE CAN GO TEN DAYS WITHOUT EATING QUITE EASILY. FASTS ARE COMMON IN ANY CIVILIZED COUNTRY, STEVE. SIXTY PERCENT OF THE BRITISH POPULATION IS CLINICALLY OBESE AT ANY ONE TIME. SHE WAS TOO FAT ANYHOW."

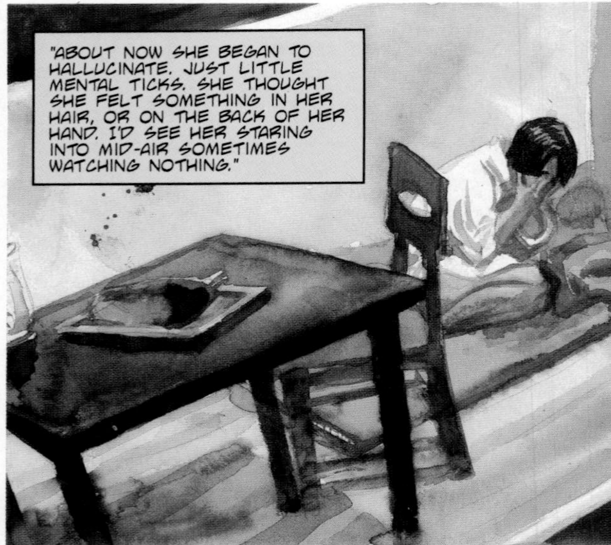
"ABOUT NOW SHE BEGAN TO HALLUCINATE. JUST LITTLE MENTAL TICKS. SHE THOUGHT SHE FELT SOMETHING IN HER HAIR, OR ON THE BACK OF HER HAND. I'D SEE HER STARING INTO MID-AIR SOMETIMES WATCHING NOTHING."

"SHE WASHED HERSELF REGULARLY. NEVER LET TWELVE HOURS GO BY WITHOUT WASHING FROM HEAD TO TOE."

"IT'S QUITE WARM IN HER LITTLE ROOM, AND THERE'S A FEW FLIES IN THERE WITH HER. THEY'VE FOUND THE MEAT, LAID THEIR EGGS. YES, IT'S RIPENING UP QUITE NICELY."

"IF THE MEAT REVOLTED WHEN IT WAS FRESH, WHAT ABOUT HER DISGUST AT ROTTED MEAT? THAT'S THE CRUX OF HER DILEMMA, ISN'T IT? THE LONGER SHE WAITS TO EAT, THE MORE DISGUSTED SHE BECOMES WITH WHAT SHE'S BEEN GIVEN TO FEED ON. SHE'S TRAPPED WITH HER OWN HORROR OF MEAT ON THE ONE HAND, AND HER DREAD OF DYING ON THE OTHER. WHICH IS GOING TO GIVE FIRST?"

STEVE WAS NO LESS TRAPPED NOW. ON THE ONE HAND, THIS JOKE HAD ALREADY GONE TOO FAR, AND QUAID'S EXPERIMENT HAD BECOME AN EXERCISE IN SADISM. ON THE OTHER HAND, HE WANTED TO KNOW HOW THE STORY ENDED. THERE WAS AN UNDENIABLE FASCINATION IN WATCHING THE WOMAN SUFFER.

STEVE SEEMED TO TASTE THE ROTTEN FLESH IN THE BACK OF HIS THROAT. HIS MIND FOUND A STENCH TO IMAGINE AND CREATED A GRAVY OF PUTRESCENCE TO RUN OVER HIS TONGUE. HOW COULD SHE DO IT?

HOW LONG NOW?
FIVE DAYS, NO SIX.
SIX DAYS.

THE THIRTY-FOURTH PHOTO WAS A BLUR. MAYBE SHE WAS BEATING HER HEAD AGAINST THE WALL-- STEVE COULDN'T BE SURE. HE WAS PAST ASKING. PART OF HIM DIDN'T WANT TO KNOW.

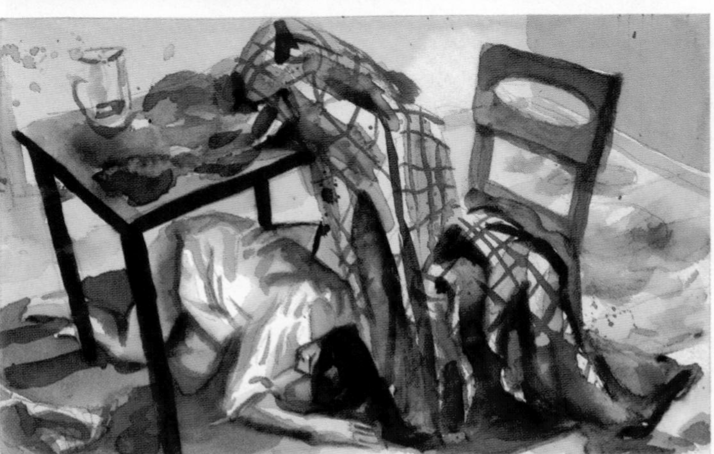

"IT STARTLED ME HOW SUDDENLY SHE GAVE IN, STEVE. ONE MOMENT SHE SEEMED TO HAVE AS MUC RESISTANCE AS EVER. TH MONOLOGUE AT THE DOO WAS THE SAME MIXTURE OF APOLOGIES AS SHE'D DELIVERED DAY IN, DAY OUT."

"THEN SHE BROKE. JUST LIKE THAT. SQUATTED UNDER THE TABLE AND ATE THE BEEF DOWN TO THE BONE, AS THOUGH IT WERE A CHOICE CUT."

"WHERE DID SHE GO?"
"SHE WANDERED DOWNSTAIRS. SHE CAME INTO THE KITCHEN, DRANK SEVERAL GLASSES OF WATER, AND SAT IN A CHAIR FOR THREE OR FOUR HOURS WITHOUT SAYING A WORD."

DID YOU SPEAK TO HER?
WHAT DID SHE SAY?
EVENTUALLY, WHEN SHE STARTED TO COME OUT OF HER FUGUE STATE. THE EXPERIMENT WAS OVER. I DIDN'T WANT TO HURT HER.
NOTHING.

NOTHING?
NOTHING AT ALL. FOR A LONG TIME I DON'T BELIEVE SHE WAS EVEN AWARE OF MY PRESENCE IN THE ROOM. THEN I COOKED SOME POTATOES, WHICH SHE ATE.
SHE DIDN'T TRY AND CALL THE POLICE?

NO, SHE KNEW WHAT I'D DONE, AND WHY I'D DONE IT. IT WASN'T PRE-PLANNED, BUT WE'D TALKED ABOUT SUCH EXPERIMENTS, IN ABSTRACT CONVERSATIONS. SHE HADN'T COME TO ANY HARM, YOU SEE. SHE'D LOST A BIT OF WEIGHT PERHAPS, BUT THAT WAS ABOUT ALL.
WHERE IS SHE NOW?

SHE LEFT THE DAY AFTER. I DON'T KNOW WHERE SHE WENT.
AND WHAT DID IT ALL PROVE?
NOTHING AT ALL, PERHAPS. BUT IT MADE AN INTERESTING START TO MY INVESTIGATIONS.

START?
THIS WAS ONLY
A *START?!*
STEPHEN--
YOU
COULD HAVE
KILLED
HER!
NO.
SHE COULD
HAVE LOST HER MIND.
BEEN UNBALANCED
PERMANENTLY!

POSSIBLY.
BUT UNLIKELY.
SHE WAS A
STRONG-WILLED
WOMAN.
BUT
YOU BROKE
HER!
YES. IT WAS
A JOURNEY SHE WAS
READY TO TAKE. WE'D TALKED
OF GOING TO FACE HER FEAR. SO
HERE WAS I, ARRANGING FOR
CHERYL TO DO JUST THAT.
NOTHING MUCH
REALLY.

YOU FORCED
HER TO DO IT. SHE
WOULDN'T HAVE GONE
OTHERWISE.
TRUE. IT
WAS AN EDUCATION
FOR HER.
SO
NOW YOU'RE A
TEACHER?
STEVE WISHED HE'D BEEN ABLE TO
KEEP THE SARCASM OUT OF HIS
VOICE. BUT IT WAS THERE. SARCASM,
ANGER, AND A LITTLE FEAR.

YES, I'M THE
TEACHER. I'M TEACHING
PEOPLE DREAD.

ARE YOU
SATISFIED WITH
WHAT YOU'VE
TAUGHT?
AND LEARNED,
STEVE. I'VE LEARNED,
TOO. IT'S A VERY EXCITING
PROSPECT--A WORLD OF FEARS TO
INVESTIGATE. ESPECIALLY WITH
INTELLIGENT SUBJECTS. EVEN
IN THE FACE OF
RATIONALIZATION--

I DON'T WANT TO HEAR ANY MORE. I'VE GOT CLASSES EARLY TOMORROW.
NO.
WHAT?

NO-- DON'T GO YET.
WHY?
STEVE'S HEART WAS RACING. HE FEARED QUAID. HE'D NEVER REALIZED HOW PROFOUNDLY.
I'VE GOT SOME MORE BOOKS TO GIVE YOU.

STEVE FELT HIS FACE FLUSH. SLIGHTLY. WHAT HAD HE THOUGHT IN THAT MOMENT? THAT QUAID WAS GOING TO BRING HIM DOWN WITH A RUGBY TACKLE AND START EXPERIMENTING ON HIS FEARS.
NO. IDIOT THOUGHTS.
I'VE GOT A BOOK ON KIERKEGAARD YOU'LL LIKE. UPSTAIRS. I'LL BE TWO MINUTES.

IT WAS THE MOMENT WHEN CHERYL FIRST PICKED UP THE ROTTING MEAT THAT FASCINATED HIM MOST. HER FACE WORE AN EXPRESSION COMPLETELY UNCHARACTERISTIC OF THE WOMAN HE HAD KNOWN. DOUBT WAS WRITTEN THERE, AND CONFUSION, AND DEEP--

--DREAD.
IT WAS QUAID'S WORD. A DIRTY WORD. AN OBSCENE WORD, ASSOCIATED FROM THIS NIGHT ON WITH QUAID'S TORTURE ON AN INNOCENT GIRL.
FOR A MOMENT, STEVE THOUGHT OF THE EXPRESSION ON HIS OWN FACE, AS HE STARED DOWN AT THE PHOTOGRAPH. WAS THERE NOT SOME OF THE SAME CONFUSION ON HIS FACE? AND PERHAPS SOME OF THE DREAD, TOO, WAITING FOR RELEASE.

HE HEARD A SOUND BEHIND HIM, TOO SOFT TO BE QUAID.
UNLESS HE WAS CREEPING.

OH, GOD, UNLESS HE WAS--

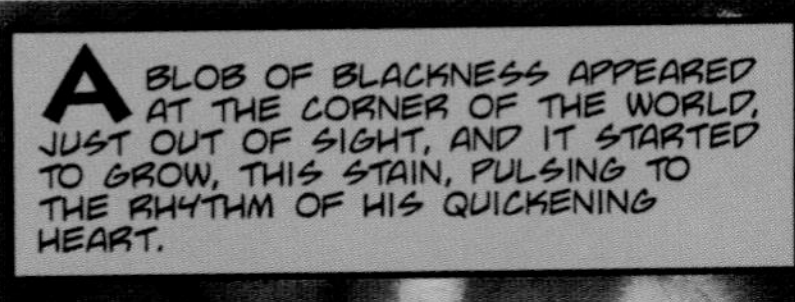
A BLOB OF BLACKNESS APPEARED AT THE CORNER OF THE WORLD, JUST OUT OF SIGHT, AND IT STARTED TO GROW, THIS STAIN, PULSING TO THE RHYTHM OF HIS QUICKENING HEART.

IN THE CENTER OF STEVE'S HEAD HE COULD SEE QUAID'S VOICE AS A VEIL. IT SAID HIS NAME.
STEPHEN
-EPHEN
-EN

THE STAIN WAS THE WORLD. THE WORLD WAS DARK, GONE AWAY.

OUT OF SIGHT, OUT OF MIND.

STEVE WAS DEAF.
ALL HE COULD HEAR WERE THE NOISES IN HIS HEAD. THE CLICKING OF HIS TEETH. THE SLUSH AND SWALLOW OF HIS PALATE. THE SOUNDS BOOMED BETWEEN HIS EARS LIKE GUNS.

HE SCREAMED UNTIL HIS THROAT FELT AS IF IT WAS BLEEDING. HE HEARD NONE OF HIS CRIES.

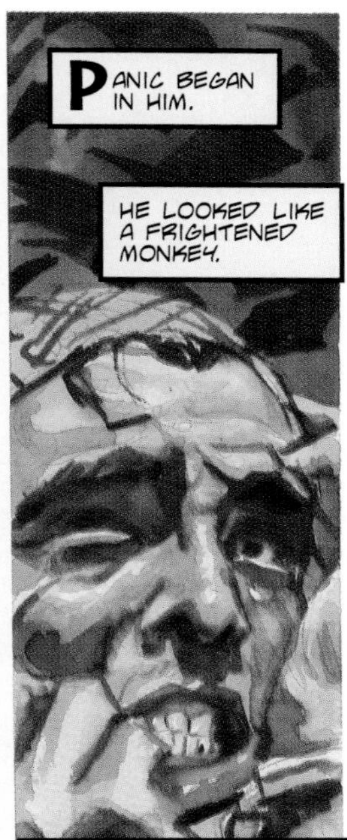
PANIC BEGAN IN HIM.
HE LOOKED LIKE A FRIGHTENED MONKEY.
ALL THE FAMILIAR, CHILDHOOD FEELINGS CAME RUSHING BACK. HE REMEMBERED THEM LIKE THE FACES OF OLD ENEMIES, THE CHITTERING LIMBS, THE SWEAT, THE NAUSEA.

THE SHOCK OF THE COLD WATER DIVERTED HIS MIND MOMENTARILY FROM THE PANIC LADDER IT WAS CLIMBING.

RELAX... RELAX...RELAX.
IN HIS HEAD, HE COULD HEAR HIS TONGUE CLICKING. HE COULD HEAR HIS MUCUS, TOO, MOVING SLUGGISHLY IN THE PANIC-CONSTRICTED PASSAGES OF HIS NOSE, BLOCKING AND UNBLOCKING IN HIS EARS. NOW HE COULD DETECT THE LOW, SOFT HISS THAT WAITED UNDER ALL THE OTHER NOISES. THE SOUND OF HIS MIND--

IT WAS LIKE THE WHITE NOISE BETWEEN STATIONS ON THE RADIO; THE SAME WHINE THAT CAME TO FETCH HIM UNDER ANESTHETIC; THE SAME NOISE THAT WOULD SOUND IN HIS EARS ON THE BORDERS OF SLEEP.

THE PHOTOGRAPHS RECORDED ALL THESE REACTIONS PRECISELY. HIS WAR WITH HYSTERIA. HIS PATHETIC ATTEMPTS TO KEEP THE FEARS FROM RESURFACING. HIS TEARS. HIS BLOODY WRISTS.

EVENTUALLY, EXHAUSTION WON OVER PANIC, AS IT HAD SO OFTEN AS A CHILD. HOW MANY TIMES HAD HE FALLEN ASLEEP WITH THE SALT-TASTE OF TEARS IN HIS NOSE AND MOUTH, UNABLE TO FIGHT ANY LONGER.
THE EXERTION HAD HEIGHTENED THE PITCH OF HIS HEADNOISES. NOW, INSTEAD OF A LULLABY, HIS BRAIN WHISTLED AND WHOOPED HIM TO SLEEP.
OBLIVION WAS GOOD.

DAMN!
QUAID WAS DISAPPOINTED. IT WAS CLEAR FROM THE SPEED OF HIS RESPONSE THAT STEPHEN GRACE WAS GOING TO BREAK VERY SOON INDEED. IN FACT, HE WAS AS GOOD AS BROKEN, ONLY A FEW HOURS INTO THE EXPERIMENT.
AND QUAID HAD BEEN RELYING ON STEPHEN. AFTER MONTHS OF PREPARING THE GROUND, IT SEEMED THAT THIS SUBJECT WAS GOING TO LOSE HIS MIND WITHOUT GIVING UP A SINGLE CLUE.

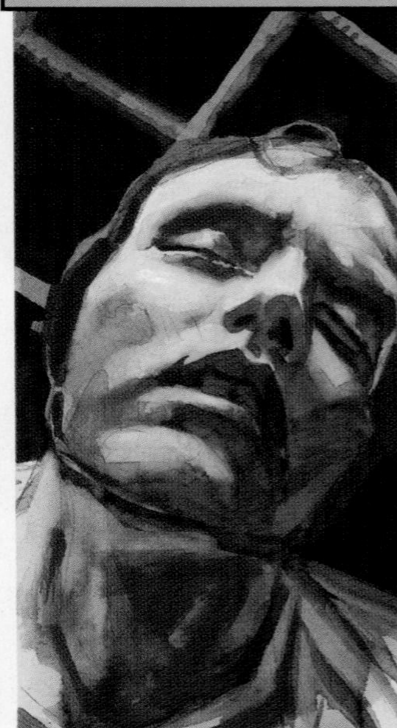
ONE WORD, ONE MISERABLE WORD WAS ALL QUAID NEEDED. A LITTLE SIGN AS TO THE NATURE OF THE EXPERIENCE. OR BETTER STILL, SOMETHING TO SUGGEST A SOLUTION, A HEALING TOTEM, A PRAYER EVEN. SURELY SOME SAVIOR COMES TO THE LIPS AS THE PERSONALITY IS SWEPT AWAY IN MADNESS? THERE MUST BE *SOMETHING*.

QUAID WAITED LIKE A CARRION BIRD AT THE SITE OF SOME ATROCITY, COUNTING THE MINUTES LEFT TO THE EXPIRING SOUL, HOPING FOR A MORSEL.

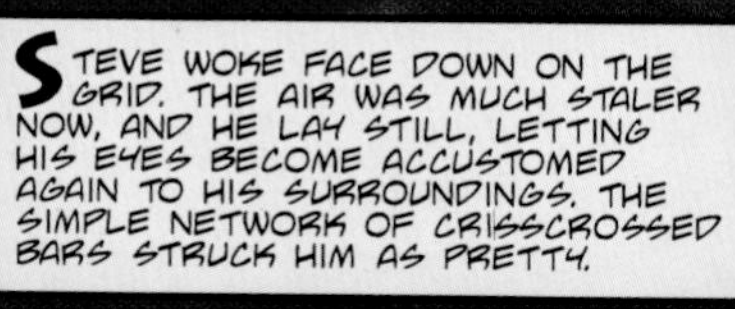
STEVE WOKE FACE DOWN ON THE GRID. THE AIR WAS MUCH STALER NOW, AND HE LAY STILL, LETTING HIS EYES BECOME ACCUSTOMED AGAIN TO HIS SURROUNDINGS. THE SIMPLE NETWORK OF CRISSCROSSED BARS STRUCK HIM AS PRETTY.

YES, PRETTY.
HE TRACED THE LINES BACK AND FORTH, 'TIL HE TIRED OF THE GAME.

THE GRID SEEMED TO ROCK A LITTLE AS HE MOVED. WAS IT LESS STABLE NOW?
SO HOT. TOO HOT. HE BEGAN TO UNDRESS. WHO WAS TO SEE?

NO, WAIT. SHOE: LATTICE: FALL. SLUGGISHLY HIS MIND MADE THE CONNECTION.
OH, POOR SHOE. MAYBE HE COULD SAVE IT IF HE TRIED.

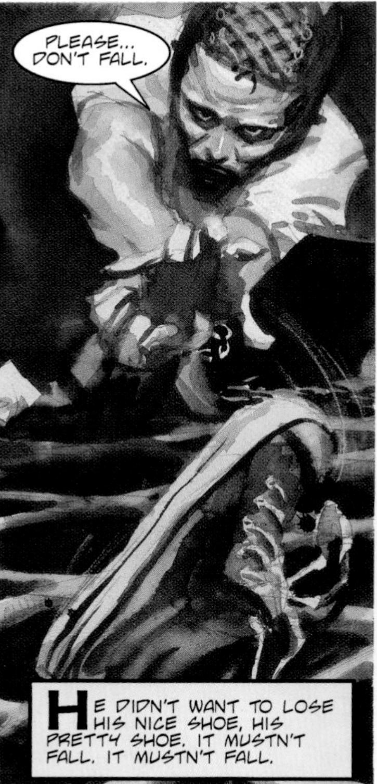
PLEASE... DON'T FALL.
HE DIDN'T WANT TO LOSE HIS NICE SHOE, HIS PRETTY SHOE. IT MUSTN'T FALL. IT MUSTN'T FALL.

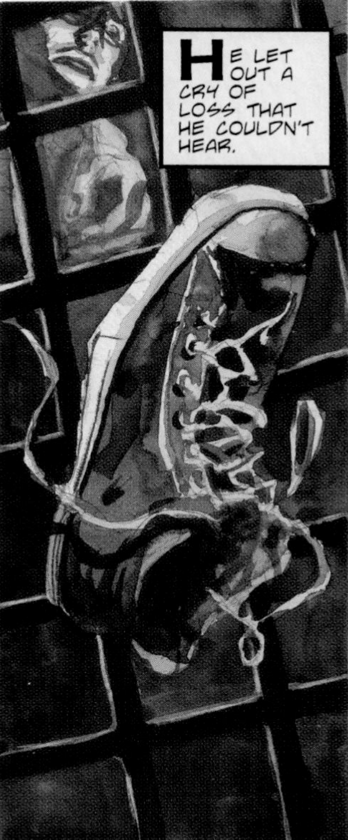
HE LET OUT A CRY OF LOSS THAT HE COULDN'T HEAR.

OH, IF ONLY HE COULD LISTEN TO THE SHOE FALLING, COUNT THE SECONDS OF ITS DESCENT. IF HE COULD ONLY HEAR IT THUD HOME AT THE BOTTOM OF THE SHAFT; AT LEAST THEN HE'D KNOW HOW FAR HE HAD TO FALL TO HIS DEATH.

I'LL GO, TOO! I'LL GO, TOO!
I'LL GO!
BENEATH HIM, THE GRID MOVED

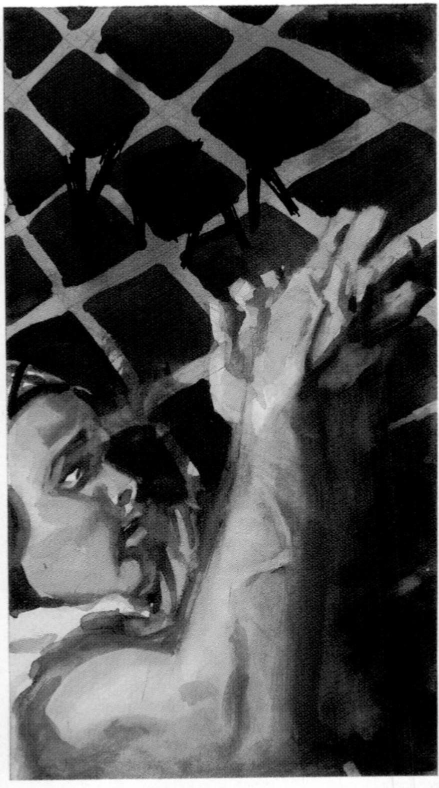

WITH SHOCK HE REALIZED HIS LIMBS WERE NO LONGER CHAINED.
HE WOULD FALL.
THE MAN WANTED HIM TO FALL. THE BAD MAN--WHAT WAS HIS NAME? QUAKE? QUAIL? QUARREL--

MAYBE HE DIDN'T WANT TO FALL AFTER HIS SHOE, AFTER ALL? MAYBE LIFE, A LITTLE MOMENT MORE OF LIFE, WAS WORTH HOLDING ON TO--
--THE DARK BEYOND THE EDGE OF THE GRID WAS SO DEEP, AND WHO COULD GUESS WHAT LURKED IN IT?
IN HIS HEAD, THE NOISE
OF PANIC MULTIPLIED. T
THUMPING OF HIS BLOO
HEART, THE STUTTER O
HIS MUCUS, THE DRY RA
OF HIS PALATE. HIS PAL
SLICK WITH SWEAT, WER
LOSING THEIR GRIP.
GRAVITY WANTED HIM. IT DEMANDED ITS RIGHT OF HIS BODY'S BULK, DEMANDED THAT HE FALL.
VILE GRAFFITI LEERED UP FROM HIS CHILDHOOD AND UNCURLED THEIR CLAWS TO SNATCH AT HIS LEGS.

MAMA.

THAT WAS THE WORD. QUAID HEARD IT PLAINLY, IN ALL ITS BANALITY, AS STEPHEN GRACE WAS DELIVERED INTO DREAD.

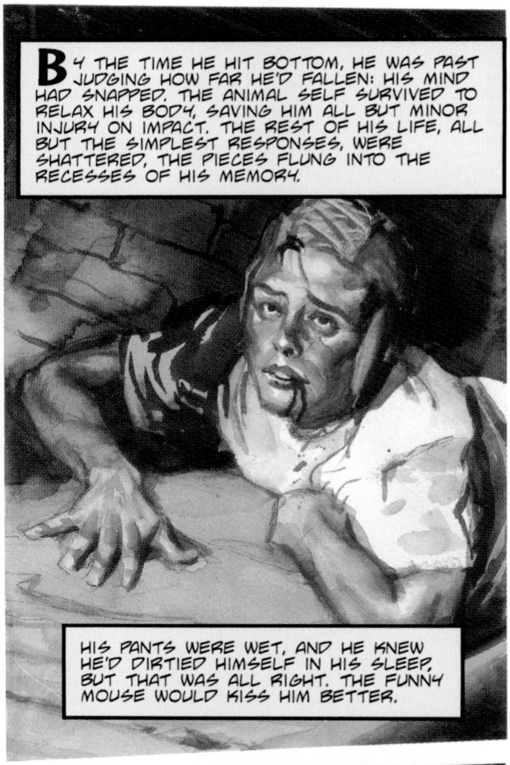

BY THE TIME HE HIT BOTTOM, HE WAS PAST JUDGING HOW FAR HE'D FALLEN: HIS MIND HAD SNAPPED. THE ANIMAL SELF SURVIVED TO RELAX HIS BODY, SAVING HIM ALL BUT MINOR INJURY ON IMPACT. THE REST OF HIS LIFE, ALL BUT THE SIMPLEST RESPONSES, WERE SHATTERED, THE PIECES FLUNG INTO THE RECESSES OF HIS MEMORY.

HIS PANTS WERE WET, AND HE KNEW HE'D DIRTIED HIMSELF IN HIS SLEEP, BUT THAT WAS ALL RIGHT. THE FUNNY MOUSE WOULD KISS HIM BETTER.

THE SHOE, THE GRID-- IT MEANT NOTHING AT ALL.

HE LET THE MOUSE GIVE HIM HIS EARS BACK, THOUGH HE DIDN'T REALLY WANT THEM. IT WAS FUN WATCHING THE WORLD WITHOUT SOUND. IT MADE HIM LAUGH.

HE WAS TIRED. HE WANTED TO SLEEP. HE WANTED HIS MAMA. BUT THE MOUSE DIDN'T SEEM TO UNDERSTAND, SO HE KICKED THE TABLE...
MAMA!

MAMA!
...AND RAN INTO THE NEXT ROOM.

OH!
IT WAS NICE WATCHING THE PAPERS FLUTTER UP AND FLUTTER DOWN. SOME OF THEM FELL FACE DOWN, SOME FACE UP. SOME WERE COVERED WITH WRITING. SOME WERE PICTURES.
HORRID PICTURES. PICTURES THAT MADE HIM FEEL VERY STRANGE.

THEY WERE ALL PICTURES OF DEAD PEOPLE, EVERY ONE OF THEM. SOME OF THE PICTURES WERE OF LITTLE CHILDREN, OTHERS WERE OF GROWN-UP CHILDREN. THERE WERE BIG CUTS IN THEIR FACES AND THEIR BODIES.
ALL AROUND THE DEAD PEOPLE WAS BLACK PAINT. NOT IN NEAT PUDDLES, BUT SPLASHED ALL AROUND, AND FINGER MARKED, AND HANDPRINTED, AND VERY MESSY.
IN THREE OR FOUR OF THE PICTURES, THE THING THAT MADE THE CUTS WAS STILL THERE. HE KNEW THE WORD FOR IT.
AXE.
THIS MAN COLLECTED PICTURES OF DEAD PEOPLE AND AXES, WHICH STEVIE THOUGHT WAS STRANGE.
BRERETON '92
THAT WAS HIS LAST THOUGHT BEFORE THE TOO-FAMILIAR SCENT OF CHLOROFORM FILLED HIS HEAD AND HE LOST CONSCIOUSNESS.

THE SORDID DOORWAY SMELT OF OLD URINE AND FRESH VOMIT. STEVE'S LEGS FELT WOBBLY. IT WAS VERY COLD. HIS THROAT HURT.
THEN HE HEARD FOOTSTEPS. IT SOUNDED LIKE THE MOUSE WAS COMING BACK. MAYBE HE'D TAKE HIM HOME.

GET UP, SON.
WHAT ARE YOU DOING DOWN THERE? I SAID, GET UP.

JESUS CHRIST. YOU'RE IN A RIGHT FUCKING STATE. WHERE DO YOU LIVE?

WHAT'S YOUR NAME?
NAME, LAD?
HE WAS TRYING TO REMEMBER. IF ONLY THE POLICEMAN WOULDN'T SHOUT.
COME ON, TAKE A HOLD OF YOURSELF.

HOME.
YOU HIGH ON SOMETHING? YOU'D BETTER MOVE ON.

MAMA, I WANT MY *MAMA*.
THE WORDS CHANGED THE ENCOUNTER ENTIRELY.

SUDDENLY THE POLICEMAN FOUND THE SPECTACLE MORE THAN DISGUSTING, MORE THAN PITIFUL. THIS LITTLE BASTARD--TOO MUCH MONEY, TOO MUCH DIRT IN HIS VEINS, TOO LITTLE DISCIPLINE.
UNGH... MAMA...
SHUT UP, SON.

YOU WANT TO BE A DERELICT, IS THAT IT?
NO... NO...
STEVE DIDN'T KNOW WHAT A DERELICT WAS. HE JUST WANTED TO MAKE THE POLICEMAN LIKE HIM.
PLEASE. TAKE ME HOME.

THERE WAS SOMETHING WRONG. THE KID HADN'T STARTED FIGHTING BACK AND CALLING FOR HIS CIVIL RIGHTS, THE WAY MOST OF THEM DID. THIS ONE JUST WEPT.
THE POLICEMAN BEGAN TO GET A BAD FEELING ABOUT THE KID. LIKE HE WAS MENTAL OR SOMETHING. AND HE'D BEATEN THE SHIT OUT OF THE LITTLE SNOT.

I'LL TAKE YOU HOME, SON. I'LL TAKE YOU HOME.
TAKE ME--
GET IN.

AT THE NIGHT HOSTEL, THEY SEARCHED STEVE'S CLOTHES FOR SOME KIND OF IDENTIFICATION, AND SCOURED HIS BODY FOR FLEAS, HIS HAIR FOR NITS.
HAVING FOUND NOTHING, THE POLICEMAN LEFT, WHICH STEVE WAS RELIEVED ABOUT. HE HADN'T LIKED THE MAN.

WELL, HE LOOKS YOUNG.
I'D PLACE HIS MENTAL AGE AT FOUR OR FIVE YEARS.
WHAT A MESS.

THEY GAVE HIM A BAR OF SOAP AND SHOWED HIM THE SHOWERS. HE DIDN'T SHAVE, THOUGH THEY'D LENT HIM A RAZOR. HE'D FORGOTTEN HOW TO DO IT.

THEN THEY GAVE HIM SOME OLD CLOTHES, WHICH HE LIKED. THEY WEREN'T SUCH BAD PEOPLE, EVEN IF THEY DID TALK ABOUT HIM AS THOUGH HE WASN'T THERE.
HE LIKED DRESSING UP. HE FELT REASSURED WITH SEVERAL THICKNESSES OF COTTON AND WOOL WRAPPED AROUND HIM.

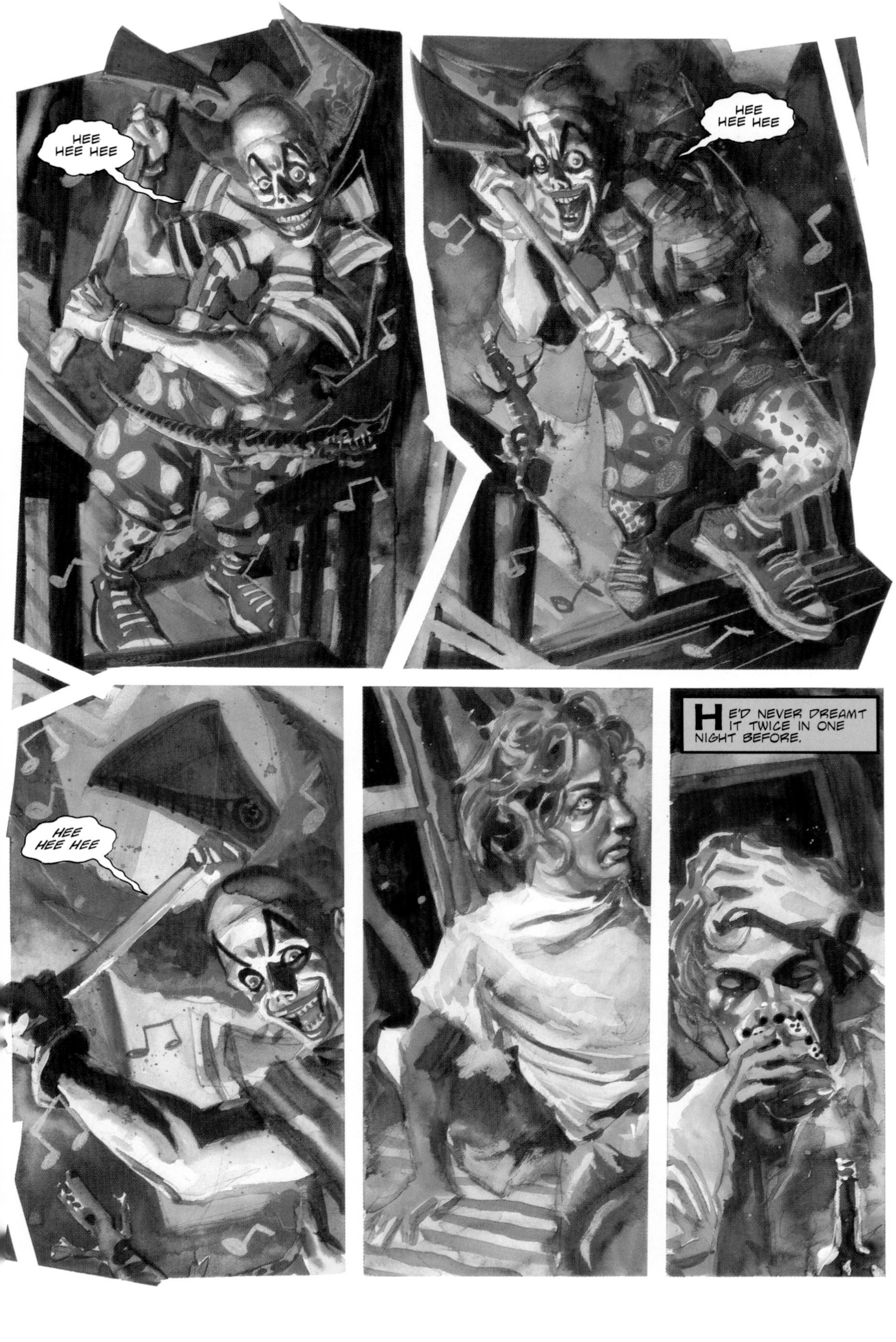

HEE HEE HEE

HEE HEE HEE

FUCK YOU! PIGLET BOY!
IT WAS THE LAST TIME OLD MAN CROWLEY WOULD BE LET IN. HE ALWAYS INVITED VIOLENCE. THIS HAD ALL THE MARKS OF A NEAR-RIOT: IT WOULD TAKE HOURS FOR THE WARDERS TO SETTLE THINGS DOWN AGAIN.

NOBODY QUESTIONED STEVE AS HE WANDERED AWAY.

A LITTLE DISTANCE AWAY HE HEARD RUNNING FEET, SHOUTS, A WHISTLE.

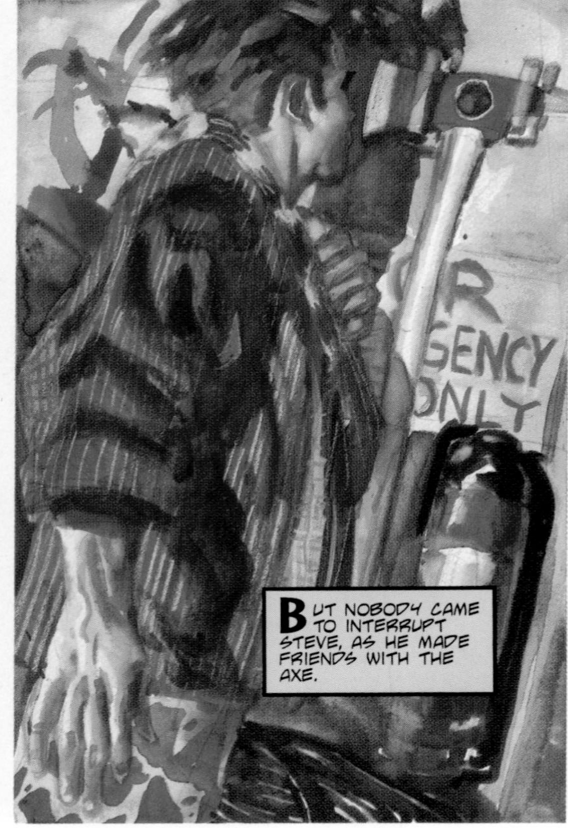
GENCY
ONLY
BUT NOBODY CAME TO INTERRUPT STEVE, AS HE MADE FRIENDS WITH THE AXE.

FIRST HE SMILED AT IT.

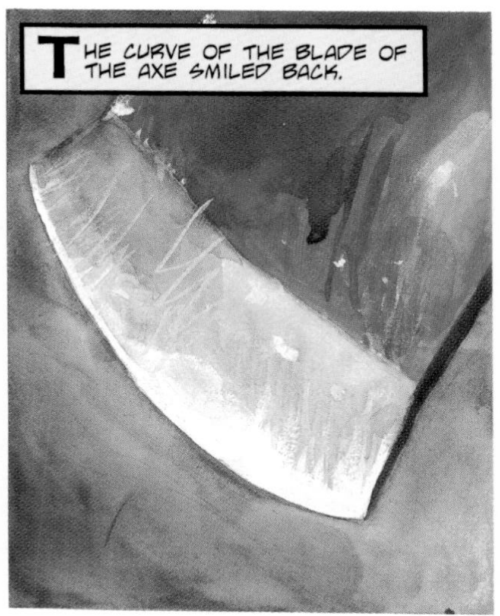
THE CURVE OF THE BLADE OF THE AXE SMILED BACK.

THEN HE TOUCHED IT.
THE AXE SEEMED TO LIKE BEING TOUCHED. IT HADN'T BEEN USED IN A LONG TIME. TOO LONG.

IT WANTED TO BE PICKED UP, AND STROKED, AND SMILED AT.

STEVE SLID IT UNDER HIS JACKET TO KEEP WARM...

...THEN HEADED OFF TO FIND HIS OTHER SHOE.

NOOOO!

IT TOOK STEVE A VERY SHORT TIME TO ORIENT HIMSELF. THERE WAS A SPRING IN HIS STEP AS HE BEGAN TO MAKE HIS WAY TO PILGRIM STREET.

HE FELT LIKE A CLOWN, DRESSED IN SO MANY BRIGHT COLORS, IN SUCH FLOPPY TROUSERS. HE WAS A COMICAL FELLOW, WASN'T HE?
HEE HEE
HE MADE HIMSELF LAUGH. HE WAS SO COMICAL.

THE WIND BEGAN TO GET INTO HIM, WHIPPING HIM UP INTO A FRENZY AS IT SCOOTED THROUGH HIS HAIR AND MADE HIS EYEBALLS AS COLD AS TWO LUMPS OF ICE IN HIS SOCKETS.
HE BEGAN TO RUN, SKIP, DANCE, CAVORT THROUGH THE STREETS, WHITE UNDER THE LIGHTS, DARK IN BETWEEN.
NOW YOU SEE ME, NOW YOU DON'T, NOW YOU SEE ME, NOW YOU--

IT WOULD SEEM TO ME, SIR, IF YOU DON'T MIND MY SAYING...
GO ON. EVEN A FOOL'S WORDS AT THIS TIME MAY SHED SOME LIGHT, NO MATTER HOW DULL IT SHINES.

THANK YOU, SIR. AHEM...WELL, IT SEEMS TO ME THAT IF THE ONE YOU SEEK REFUSES TO SHOW HIMSELF THEN YOU MUST GIVE HIM NO CHOICE.
DEFINE. BE SPECIFIC.
PERHAPS TO WIN YOUR WAY BACK INTO THE ARMS OF OUR MAKER YOU MUST PERHAPS PUT YOUR SOUL IN DIRECT JEOPARDY.

THE NOTION HAD SOME MERIT.
SUPPOSE I COULD CONTRIVE A MEETING WITH SATAN, THE ARCHFIEND. SEEING ME *IN EXTREMIS*, WOULD NOT GOD BE OBLIGATED TO STEP IN AND DELIVER ME TO THE FOLD?
IT WAS A FINE PLOT, BUT HOW WAS HE TO REALIZE IT?

THE DEVIL DID NOT JUST COME AT A CALL, EVEN FOR A TYCOON SUCH AS GREGORIUS.
BUT THERE HAD TO BE A WAY, AND GREGORIUS WOULD FIND IT.

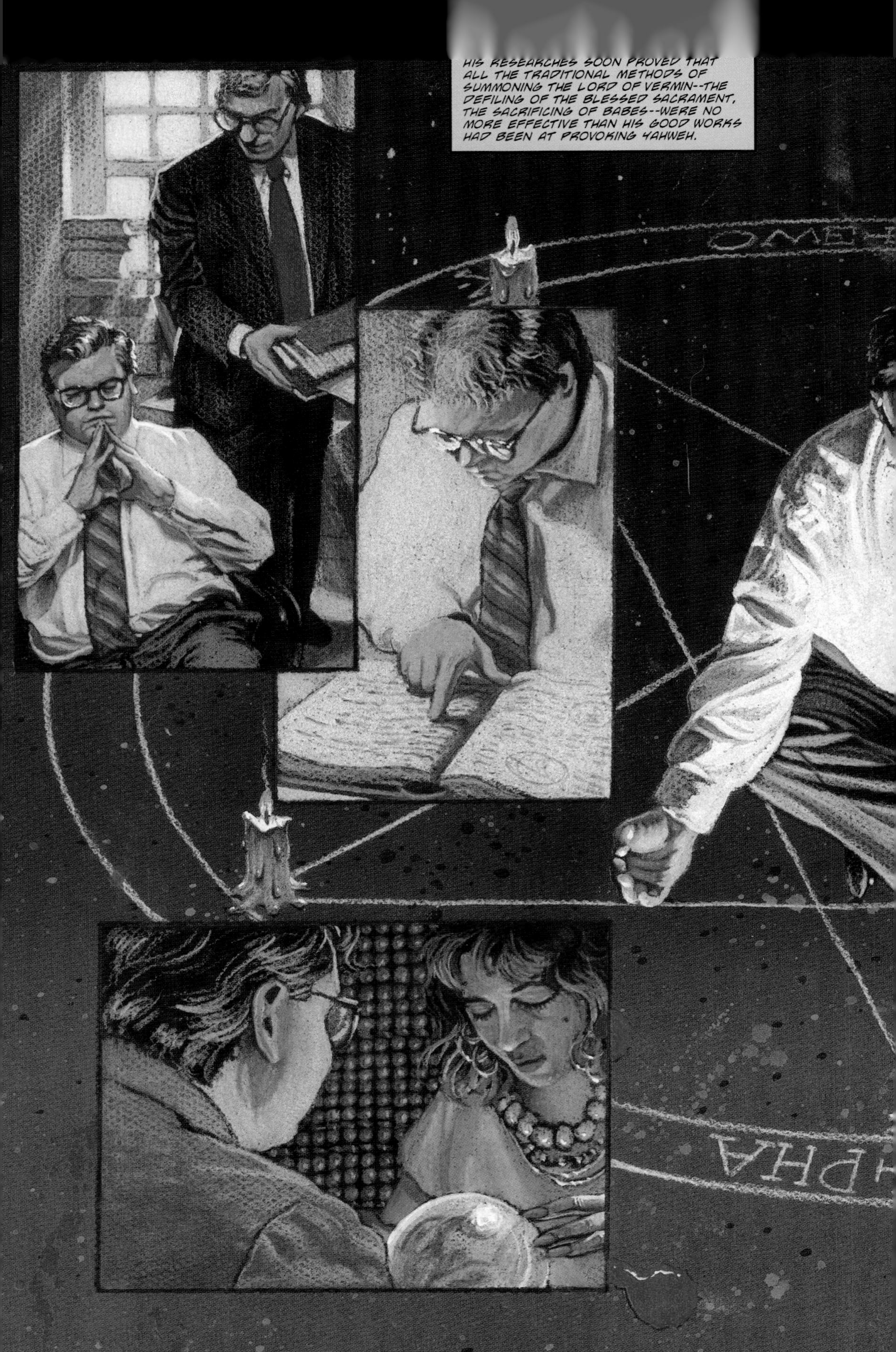
HIS RESEARCHES SOON PROVED THAT ALL THE TRADITIONAL METHODS OF SUMMONING THE LORD OF VERMIN--THE DEFILING OF THE BLESSED SACRAMENT, THE SACRIFICING OF BABES--WERE NO MORE EFFECTIVE THAN HIS GOOD WORKS HAD BEEN AT PROVOKING YAHWEH.

IT WAS ONLY AFTER A YEAR OF DELIBERATION THAT HE FINALLY FELL UPON HIS MASTER PLAN.
HE WOULD ARRANGE TO HAVE BUILT A HELL ON EARTH, A MODERN INFERNO SO MONSTROUS THAT THE TEMPTER WOULD BE TEMPTED, AND COME TO ROOST THERE LIKE A CUCKOO IN AN USURPED NEST.

HE SEARCHED HIGH AND LOW FOR AN ARCHITECT AND FOUND, LANGUISHING IN A MADHOUSE OUTSIDE FLORENCE, A MAN CALLED LEOPARDO, WHOSE PLANS FOR MUSSOLINI'S PALACES HAD A LUNATIC GRANDEUR THAT SUITED GREGORIUS' PROJECT PERFECTLY.

LEOPARDO WAS TAKEN FROM HIS CELL-- A FETID, WRETCHED OLD MAN--AND GIVEN HIS DREAMS AGAIN. HIS GENIUS FOR THE PRODIGIOUS HAD NOT DESERTED HIM.

IN ORDER TO FUEL HIS INVENTION, THE GREAT LIBRARIES OF THE WORLD WERE SCOURED FOR DESCRIPTIONS OF HELLS BOTH SECULAR AND METAPHYSICAL.
MUSEUM VAULTS WERE RANSACKED FOR FORBIDDEN IMAGES OF MARTYRDOM.

NO STONE WAS LEFT UNTURNED IF IT WAS SUSPECTED SOMETHING PERVERSE WAS CONCEALED BENEATH.
THE FINISHED DESIGNS OWED SOMETHING TO DE SADE AND TO DANTE, AND SOMETHING MORE TO FREUD AND KRAFFT-EBING, BUT THERE WAS ALSO MUCH THERE THAT NO MIND HAD CONCEIVED OF BEFORE, OR AT LEAST EVER DARED TO PUT ON PAPER.

A SITE IN NORTH AFRICA WAS CHOSEN, AND WORK ON GREGORIUS' NEW HELL BEGAN.

EVERYTHING ABOUT THE PROJECT BROKE THE RECORDS. ITS FOUNDATIONS WERE VASTER, ITS WALLS THICKER, ITS PLUMBING MORE ELABORATE THAN ANY EDIFICE HITHERTO ATTEMPTED. GREGORIUS WATCHED ITS SLOW CONSTRUCTION WITH AN ENTHUSIASM HE HAD NOT TASTED SINCE HIS FIRST YEARS AS AN EMPIRE BUILDER.

NEEDLESS TO SAY, HE WAS WIDELY THOUGHT TO HAVE LOST HIS MIND. FRIENDS HE HAD KNOWN FOR YEARS REFUSED TO ASSOCIATE WITH HIM. SEVERAL OF HIS COMPANIES COLLAPSED WHEN INVESTORS TOOK FRIGHT AT REPORTS OF HIS INSANITY.
HE DIDN'T CARE. HIS PLAN COULD NOT FAIL.

THE DEVIL WOULD BE BOUND TO COME, IF ONLY OUT OF CURIOSITY TO SEE THIS LEVIATHAN BUILT IN HIS NAME, AND WHEN HE DID...
...GREGORIUS WOULD BE WAITING.

THE WORK TOOK FOUR YEARS AND THE BETTER PART OF GREGORIUS' FORTUNE.
THE FINISHED BUILDING WAS THE SIZE OF HALF A DOZEN CATHEDRALS AND BOASTED EVERY FACILITY THE ANGEL OF THE PIT COULD DESIRE.

FIRES BURNED BEHIND ITS WALLS, SO THAT TO WALK IN MANY OF ITS CORRIDORS WAS ALMOST UNENDURABLE AGONY. THE ROOMS OFF THOSE CORRIDORS WERE FITTED WITH EVERY IMAGINABLE DEVICE OF PERSECUTION THAT THE GENIUS OF SATAN'S TORTURES BE GIVEN FAIR EMPLOY.
THERE WERE OVENS LARGE ENOUGH TO CREMATE FAMILIES, POOLS DEEP ENOUGH TO DROWN GENERATIONS.
THE NEW HELL WAS AN ATROCITY WAITING TO HAPPEN: A CELEBRATION OF INHUMANITY THAT ONLY LACKED ITS FIRST CAUSE.

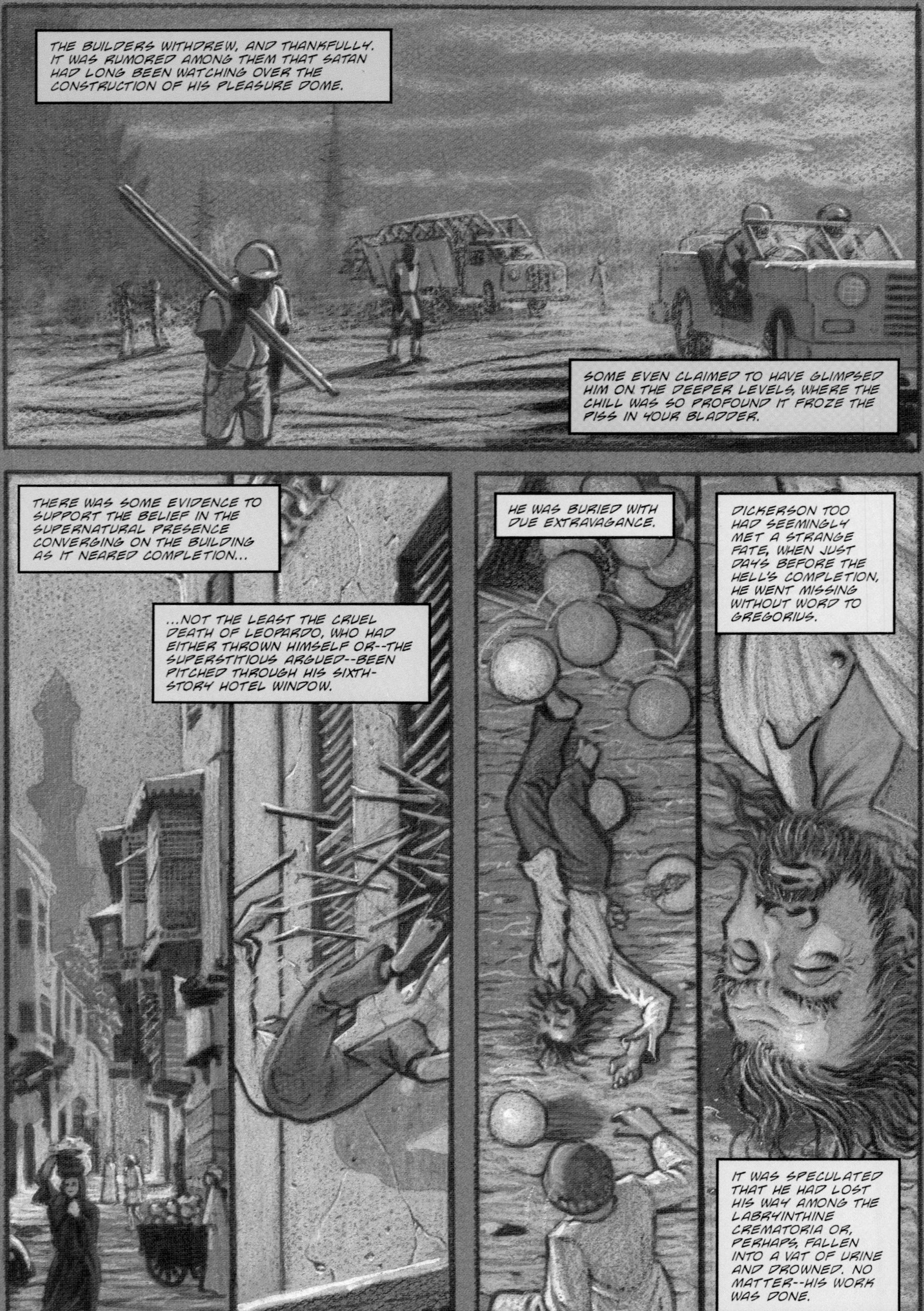

THERE WAS SOME EVIDENCE TO SUPPORT THE BELIEF IN THE SUPERNATURAL PRESENCE CONVERGING ON THE BUILDING AS IT NEARED COMPLETION...

...NOT THE LEAST THE CRUEL DEATH OF LEOPARDO, WHO HAD EITHER THROWN HIMSELF OR--THE SUPERSTITIOUS ARGUED--BEEN PITCHED THROUGH HIS SIXTH-STORY HOTEL WINDOW.

HE WAS BURIED WITH DUE EXTRAVAGANCE.

DICKERSON TOO HAD SEEMINGLY MET A STRANGE FATE, WHEN JUST DAYS BEFORE THE HELL'S COMPLETION, HE WENT MISSING WITHOUT WORD TO GREGORIUS.

IT WAS SPECULATED THAT HE HAD LOST HIS WAY AMONG THE LABRYINTHINE CREMATORIA OR, PERHAPS, FALLEN INTO A VAT OF URINE AND DROWNED. NO MATTER--HIS WORK WAS DONE.

SO NOW, ALONE IN HELL, GREGORIUS WAITED.

HE DID NOT HAVE TO WAIT LONG.

HE HAD BEEN THERE A DAY, NO MORE, WHEN HE HEARD NOISES FROM THE LOWER DEPTHS.

ANTICIPATION BRIMMING, HE WENT IN SEARCH OF THE NOISES' SOURCE, BUT FOUND ONLY THE ROILING OF EXCREMENT BATHS AND THE RATTLING OF OVENS.

HE RETURNED TO HIS SUITE OF CHAMBERS ON THE NINTH LEVEL AND WAITED.

THE NOISES CAME AGAIN: AGAIN HE WENT IN SEARCH OF THEIR SOURCE: AGAIN HE CAME AWAY DISAPPOINTED.

THE DISTURBANCES DID NOT ABATE, HOWEVER.

IN THE DAYS THAT FOLLOWED SCARCELY TEN MINUTES WOULD PASS WITHOUT HIS HEARING SOME SOUND OF OCCUPANCY.

THE PRINCE OF DARKNESS WAS HERE, GREGORIUS HAD NO DOUBT OF IT, BUT HE WAS KEEPING TO THE SHADOWS.

GREGORIUS WAS CONTENT TO PLAY ALONG. IT WAS THE DEVIL'S PARTY AFTER ALL. HIS TO PLAY WHATEVER HE CHOSE.

UT DURING THE LONG AND OFTEN LONELY
ONTHS THAT FOLLOWED, GREGORIUS
EARIED OF THIS HIDE AND SEEK AND
EGAN TO DEMAND THAT SATAN SHOW
IMSELF.

I KNOW YOU'RE HERE! COME FORWARD, DAMN YOU!

HIS VOICE RANG UNANSWERED DOWN THE DESERTED CORRIDORS, HOWEVER, UNTIL HIS THROAT WAS BRUISED WITH SHOUTING.

THEREAFTER HE WENT ABOUT HIS SEARCHES STEALTHILY, HOPING TO CATCH HIS TENANT UNAWARE.

BUT THE APOSTATE ANGEL ALWAYS FLITTED AWAY BEFORE GREGORIUS COULD STEP WITHIN SIGHT OF HIM.

THE DEVIL HAD COME, HADN'T HE?

WASN'T THAT HIS FINGERPRINT ON THE DOOR HANDLE? THE TURD ON THE STAIRS?

THEY WOULD PLAY THE WAITING GAME, IT SEEMED, HE AND SATAN, CHASING EACH OTHER'S TAILS THROUGH ICE AND FIRE AND FIRE AND ICE AGAIN. GREGORIUS TOLD HIMSELF TO BE PATIENT.

SOONER OR LATER THE FIEND WOULD SHOW HIS FACE, AND GREGORIUS WOULD SPIT ON IT.

THE WORLD OUTSIDE WENT ON ITS WAY, AND GREGORIUS WAS CONSIGNED TO THE COMPANY OF OTHER RECLUSES WHO HAD BEEN RUINED BY WEALTH.

HIS FOLLY, AS IT WAS KNOWN, WAS NOT ENTIRELY WITHOUT VISITORS, HOWEVER. THERE WERE A FEW WHO HAD LOVED HIM TOO MUCH TO FORGET HIM WHO DARED THE GATES OF THE NEW HELL.

THESE VISITORS MADE THE JOURNEY WITHOUT ANNOUNCING THEIR INTENTIONS, FEARING THE DISAPPROVAL OF THEIR FRIENDS.

THE INVESTIGA-TIONS INTO THEIR SUBSEQUENT DISAPPEARANCE NEVER REACHED AS FAR AS NORTH AFRICA.

AND IN HIS FOLLY GREGORIUS STILL CHASED THE SERPENT, AND THE SERPENT STILL ELUDED HIM, LEAVING ONLY MORE AND MORE TERRIBLE SIGNS OF HIS OCCUPANCY AS THE MONTHS WENT BY.
...AND YOU KNOW THE REST.
WE WANT TO HEAR FROM YOUR MOUTH, IN YOUR WORDS.
FROM WHAT I'VE GATHERED, IT WAS THE WIFE OF ONE OF THE MISSING VISITORS WHO FINALLY DISCOVERED THE TRUTH AND ALERTED THE AUTHORITIES.
THIS WAS WHEN THEY PUT GREGORIUS UNDER SURVEILLANCE, AND THEN THOSE MEN, THE POLICE, WENT INTO THE NEW HELL...

WITHOUT MAINTENANCE THE FOLLY HAD BEGUN TO DETERIORATE BADLY.
THE LIGHTS HAD FAILED ON MANY OF THE LEVELS. ITS WALLS COOLED, ITS PITCH PITS SOLIDIFIED.
BUT AS THE OFFICERS ADVANCED IN SEARCH OF GREGORIUS THEY CAME UPON AMPLE EVIDENCE THAT DESPITE ITS DECREPIT CONDITION, THE NEW HELL WAS IN GOOD WORKING ORDER.
THERE WERE BODIES EVERYWHERE.
THERE WERE HUMAN REMAINS SEATED AND STRUNG, GOUGED AND PRICKED AND SLIT TO DEATH.

THEIR TERROR GREW WITH EVERY DOOR THEY PRESSED OPEN, EVERY ABOMINATION THEIR FEVERED EYES FELL UPON.
TWO OF THE FOUR WHO CROSSED THE THRESHOLD NEVER REACHED THE CHAMBER AT ITS CENTER.
TERROR OVERTOOK THEM ON THEIR WAY AND THEY FLED...
...ONLY TO BE WAYLAID IN SOME CHOKED PASSAGE-WAY AND ADDED TO THE HUNDREDS WHO HAD PERISHED IN THE FOLLY SINCE SATAN HAD TAKEN RESIDENCE.
THERE WAS NO SIGN OF SATAN, OF COURSE. THERE WAS ONLY GREGORIUS. THE MASTER BUILDER, FINDING NO ONE TO INHABIT THE HOUSE HE'D SWEATED OVER, HAD OCCUPIED IT HIMSELF.
HE HAD WITH HIM A FEW DISCIPLES WHOM HE'D MUSTERED OVER THE YEARS. THEY, LIKE HIM, SEEMED UNREMARKABLE CREATURES. BUT THERE WAS NOT A TORTURE DEVICE IN THE BUILDING THEY HAD NOT MADE THOROUGH AND MERCILESS USE OF.
GREGORIOUS DID NOT RESIST HIS ARREST.
INDEED HE SEEMED PLEASED THAT HE WOULD HAVE A PLATFORM FROM WHICH HE COULD BOAST HIS BUTCHERIES.

LATER AT HIS TRIAL, HE SPOKE FREELY OF HIS AMBITION AND HIS APPETITE: AND OF HOW MUCH MORE BLOOD HE WOULD SPILL IF THEY WOULD ONLY SET HIM FREE TO DO SO.
"ENOUGH TO DROWN ALL BELIEF AND ITS DELUSIONS-- AND STILL I'D NOT BE SATISFIED. FOR GOD IS ROTTING IN PARADISE, AND SATAN IN THE ABYSS, AND WHO IS TO STOP ME?"

HE WAS MUCH REVILED DURING THE TRIAL, AND LATER IN THE ASYLUM WHERE, UNDER SOME SUSPICIOUS CIRCUMSTANCES, HE DIED BARELY TWO MONTHS LATER.

THE VATICAN EXPUNGED ALL REPORT OF HIM FROM ITS RECORDS.
THE SEMINARIES FOUNDED IN HIS UNHOLY NAME WERE DISSOLVED.

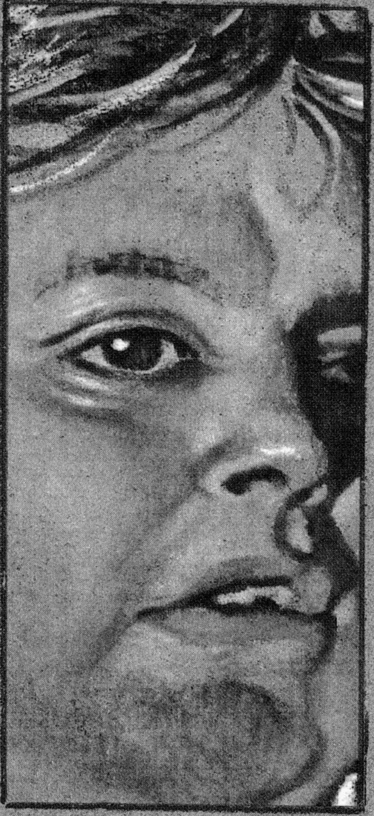
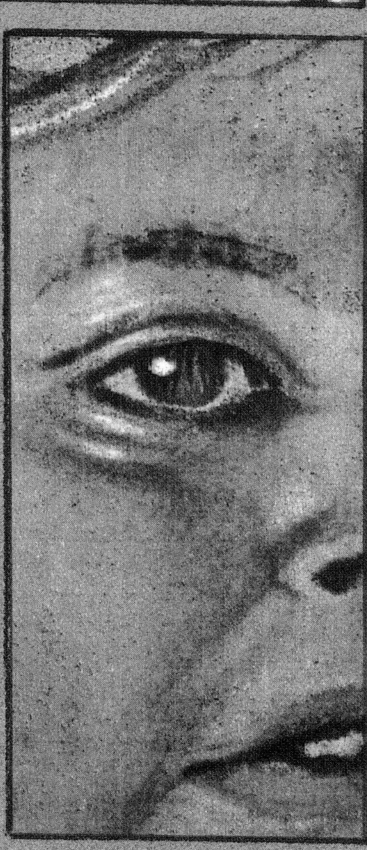

BUT THERE WERE THOSE AMONG THE CARDINALS WHO COULD NOT PUT GREGORIUS' UNREPENTANT MALICE OUT OF THEIR HEADS.
...AND THAT'S ALL I KNOW. THAT'S ALL I CAN TELL YOU, I SWEAR.
THERE IS ONE QUESTION REMAINING...WHERE WERE YOU ALL THE TIME YOU WERE SAID TO BE GONE?

I...I WAS THERE. I NEVER LEFT. I HID FROM GREGORIUS. NOT BECAUSE I WAS AFRAID, NOT AT ALL. I SIMPLY SAW WHAT HE WAS AND KNEW HE NEEDED TO BE ALONE TO BECOME IT.
AND THOSE CARDINALS, IN THE PRIVACY OF THEIR DOUBTS, WONDERED IF GREGORIUS HAD NOT SUCCEEDED IN HIS STRATEGY.

WELL, I SUPPOSE THAT'S ABOUT ALL, THEN.
THEY WONDERED IF, IN GIVING UP ALL HOPE OF ANGELS, FALLEN OR OTHERWISE, GREGORIUS HAD NOT BECOME ONE HIMSELF.

BAM
OR ALL THAT EARTH COULD BEAR OF SUCH A PHENOMENA.

The End

ALSO PUBLISHED BY ECLIPSE GRAPHIC NOVELS

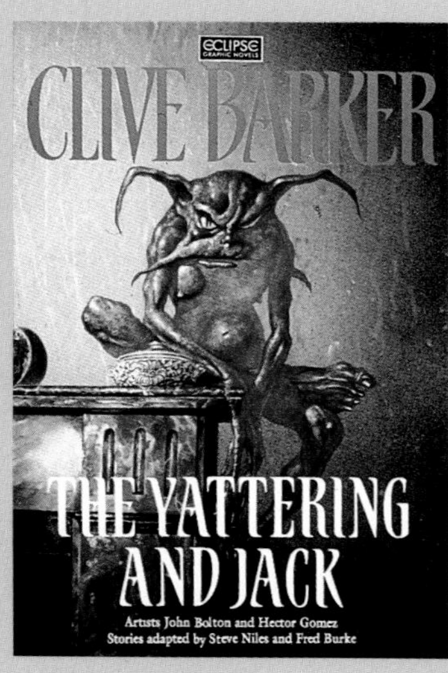

CLIVE BARKER'S

THE YATTERING AND JACK

Adapted by Steve Niles
Illustrated by John Bolton

A DARKLY HILARIOUS and weirdly perceptive tale of the devil at work from the acclaimed fantasist and master of horror fiction, Clive Barker.

Beelzebub sends his underling the Yattering to claim the soul of Jack Polo, pickle salesman. But in the Polo residence where the Yattering is bound, nothing doing. Polo's response, even to disaster, is merely to sigh, '*Que sera sera*'. The Yattering is going crazy. He must goad Polo to lunacy, the Old One insists. Polo was promised by his mother to the Lord of the Flies. And what match is a chronically dull pickle salesman for hell's own spawn . . . ? Find out.

Included in the same volume, a graphic adaptation of Clive Barker's short story *How Spoilers Bleed,* adapted by Steve Niles and Fred Burke, and illustrated by Hector Gomez. It tells of the gory revenge visited on white destroyers of the Brazilian jungle by the dying indigenous people of the Amazon basin. It is a punishment that fits the crime, incredibly unpleasant . . .

Clive Barker's bestselling works of fiction include *The Books of Blood*, *The Damnation Game*, *Weaveworld*, *Cabal*, *The Great and Secret Show*, *The Hellbound Heart*, *Imajica* and *The Thief of Always.* Not only is he prodigiously talented as a writer, he also produces and directs memorable films such as the *Hellraiser* trilogy, *Nightbreed* and *Candyman*, and is himself a spectacular visual artist. The illustrators he chooses to work with, therefore, John Bolton and Hector Gomez, are equally brilliant.

NEIL GAIMAN

MIRACLEMAN: THE GOLDEN AGE

Illustrated by Mark Buckingham

NEIL GAIMAN'S spectacular, mysterious, luminously strange and compelling saga of the all-British superhero and deity, Miracleman. *The Golden Age* is the age of miracles unimagined. It is the age of gods among men. It is the age of truth in which everything is what it seems, and nothing is as it was imagined.

'A work that transforms the superhero genre into something strange, wonderful, and politic. Excellent stuff!'

ALAN MOORE

MIRACLEMAN was given new life by Alan Moore, known as the King of the graphic novel, in the early 1980s. His and Gaiman's work is assessed in the critique below by Samuel R. Delany, author of *Dhalgren*, the *Nevèrÿon* series, and other science fiction masterpieces.

'Moore and Gaiman are the two writers who have done more to change the idea of what comics are and can be than anyone since . . . well, certainly since I started reading them in the 1940s. Reading Moore, followed by Gaiman, I found myself for the first time deeply, consistently, intensely interested in these comic book writers *as writers.* With that interest came a revision in the idea of what comics could be; they could be *written*, not just in a craftsman-like manner adequate to the visuals. The writing could be brilliant in itself. Here were writers with the range of language from silence to song - the whole of language with which to put across their stories. And the stories themselves! Gaiman's six entwined tales in *The Golden Age* come like sapphires afloat on a super-cooled liquid. They unfold like haiku. The voices they speak with are real. Their lambent characters, yearning both for bits of yesterday and portents of tomorrow, will linger with you long.'

SAMUEL R. DELANY